Contents

Published by
CJ FALLON
Ground Floor – Block B
Liffey Valley Office Campus
Dublin 22

First edition May 2005

This reprint May 2012

Printed in Ireland by
Naas Printing Limited
South Main Street
Naas
Co Kildare

1. Revision

Mental Computation

1. $38 + 9 =$ _____
2. $46 + 20 =$ _____
3. $62 + 35 =$ _____
4. $55 - 8 =$ _____
5. $79 - 20 =$ _____
6. $96 - 24 =$ _____
7. $(8 \times 7) + 5 =$ _____
8. $(9 \times 8) + 6 =$ _____
9. $(10 \times 9) + 8 =$ _____
10. $63 \div 7 =$ _____
11. $80 \div 8 =$ _____
12. $54 \div 9 =$ _____
13. $\frac{3}{8}$ of $40 =$ _____
14. $\frac{5}{6}$ of $24 =$ _____
15. $\frac{4}{9}$ of $36 =$ _____

Score $\boxed{}$ /15

Written Computation

1.
```
   346
   287
 + 139
 _____
```

2.
```
   2463
   1937
 + 4389
 _____
```

3.
```
   €18·46
   €27·59
 + €34·78
 _____
```

4.
```
   €28·09
   €34·78
 + €23·96
 _____
```

5.
```
   835
 - 678
 _____
```

6.
```
   6352
 - 4573
 _____
```

7.
```
   €47·32
 - €29·65
 _____
```

8.
```
   €70·23
 - €36·45
 _____
```

9.
```
   438
 ×   7
 _____
```

10.
```
   567
 ×   8
 _____
```

11.
```
   794
 ×   6
 _____
```

12.
```
   586
 ×   9
 _____
```

13.
```
   235
 ×  29
 _____
```

14.
```
   148
 ×  63
 _____
```

15.
```
   237
 ×  24
 _____
```

16.
```
   156
 ×  47
 _____
```

17. $4\overline{)756}$

_____

18. $7\overline{)952}$

_____

19. $9\overline{)876}$

_____ R_____

20. $8\overline{)975}$

_____ R_____

Score $\boxed{}$ /20

1

Mental Problems

1. 119 girls and 100 boys attend a school.
   How many children altogether attend? _____

2. A farmer had 165 animals.
   He sold 40 of them.
   How many animals had he left? _____

3. Joe has €4·30. Jane has €2·50 more than Joe.
   How much money has Jane? _____

4. What change had Ann from €10·00
   when she bought the football? _____

   €7·40

5. How much would 10 oranges cost? _____

   16c

6. Ten biros cost €4·50.
   How much should 20 biros cost? _____

7. What must be added to 10 times 53 to make 600? _____

8. Barry has 56 stamps. Barbara has $\frac{7}{8}$ of that number.
   How many stamps has Barbara? _____

   50c

9. Jim has 35 cards,
   Jane has 12 more than that.
   How many cards have they between them? _____

10. A farmer had 72 sheep. She sold $\frac{1}{9}$ of them.
    How many sheep had she left? _____

11. $\frac{3}{4}$ of the apples in a box were green.
    If there were 36 green apples,
    how many apples were there in the box altogether? _____

12. Six bars cost €2·30.
    How much should 18 bars cost? _____

    Choco

Score ___ /12

2

Written Problems

1. There are 2347 beech trees, 956 oak trees and 1938 ash trees in a forest. How many trees altogether are there in the forest? _____

2. There are 8364 people living in Newtown. There are 5478 people living in Oldtown. How many more people live in Newtown than in Oldtown? _____

3. A hurley costs €16·35. Pat has saved €9·78. How much more does he need to buy the hurley? _____

4. There are 238 pages in a book. How many pages altogether are there in 9 such books? _____

5. A farmer had 152 cattle. She sold $\frac{3}{8}$ of them. How many cattle did she sell? _____

6. A box holds 96 oranges. How many oranges will 18 boxes hold? _____

7. A bicycle costs €96·85. Ann had €53·62. Her Mam gave her €24·36. How much more does she need to buy the bicycle? _____

8. A cinema ticket costs €7·85. What is the total cost of 8 cinema tickets? _____

9. Frank has €58·75. How much more does he need to buy 7 footballs costing €9·69 each? _____

10. $\frac{3}{8}$ of the cars in a car park were black. If there were 144 black cars, how many cars altogether were in the car park? _____

11. A box of chocolates cost €4·85. What change did I get from €50 when I bought 9 boxes? _____

12. Five packets of sweets cost €9·85. How much should two packets of sweets cost? _____

Score [/12]

3

2. Revision

Mental Computation

1. $1425 + 300 =$ _____
2. $2347 + 600 =$ _____
3. $7850 + 400 =$ _____
4. $1876 - 400 =$ _____
5. $3975 - 700 =$ _____
6. $4150 - 200 =$ _____
7. €5 − €3·45 = _____
8. $2\frac{1}{4}$ m = _____ cm
9. 2·7km = _____ m
10. 3·28kg = _____ g
11. $2\frac{3}{10}$ l = _____ ml
12. $2\frac{1}{2}$ hours = _____ mins
13. 0·3 of 40 = _____
14. 0·7 of 60 = _____
15. $1\frac{3}{4}$ hours = _____ mins

Score ☐ /15

Written Computation

1.
```
  €4·39
×    6
──────
```

2.
```
  €7·68
×    8
──────
```

3.
```
  €6·84
×    9
──────
```

4.
```
  €9·78
×    7
──────
```

5.
```
  13·46km
  24·58km
+ 19·74km
─────────
```

6.
```
  23·67kg
  15·96kg
+ 34·82kg
─────────
```

7.
```
  27·38l
  18·79l
+ 26·43l
────────
```

8.
```
hrs mins
  3   49
+ 2   56
────────
```

9.
```
  57·34km
− 29·68km
─────────
```

10.
```
  72·63kg
− 37·85kg
─────────
```

11.
```
  60·43l
− 27·56l
────────
```

12.
```
  €70·00
− €26·38
────────
```

13.
```
  269
× 28
─────
```

14.
```
  187
× 35
─────
```

15.
```
  234
× 29
─────
```

16.
```
  258
× 37
─────
```

17. $6\,\lvert\,€9·42$

18. $5\,\lvert\,8·95km$

19. $6\,\lvert\,8·58kg$

20. $7\,\lvert\,9·59l$

Score ☐ /20

4

Mental Problems

1. Joe had €10. He bought a scarf.
   What change did he get? _____

2. $\frac{5}{9}$ of the 72 children in a school were girls.
   How many were girls? _____

3. A farmer had 90 animals. 0·3 of these were cows.
   How many cows had he? _____

4. A container holds 650ml.
   How much less than a litre does it hold? _____

5. A box of sweets weighed 1·6kg.
   When 900g of the sweets were sold,
   what weight of sweets was left in the box? _____

6. When the runners had completed
   2·8km of a 3000 metre race,
   how many metres had they to go? _____

7. What is the cost of 2kg of meat at €4·50 per 500 grammes? _____

8. 0·7 of the people at a match were children.
   If 42 children attended, how many people altogether
   were at the match? _____

9. Jack spent 0·45 of his money in a shop.
   What decimal fraction of his money had he left? _____

10. A TV programme started at 3:45.
    If the programme lasted 40 minutes,
    at what time did it end? _____

11. 15cm
    9cm
    What is the perimeter of this rectangle? _____

12. A room is 5 metres long and 4 metres wide.
    What will it cost to carpet the room
    at €10 per square metre? _____

Score [/12]

5

Written Problems

1. There are 185 straws in a box.
   How many straws are there in 27 boxes? _____

2. There are 864 trees in a forest. $\frac{5}{9}$ of them are beech trees.
   How many beech trees are in the forest? _____

3. Find the total weight of 3 boxes that weigh
   2·65kg, $1\frac{9}{10}$kg and 3kg 480g respectively. _____

4. Edward cycled 3km 650m. Elaine cycled 780m further than that.
   What was the total distance cycled by the two of them? _____

5. $\frac{4}{9}$ of the children in a school are girls.
   If there are 148 girls, how many children attend the school? _____

6. Peter drinks 2·65 litres of water each day.
   How many litres does he drink in a week? _____

7. David had €50.
   He spent €18·75 in one shop and €19·54 in another.
   How much had he left? _____

8. A wooden plank 8m 76cm was cut into 6 equal pieces.
   How long was each piece? _____

9. A bus left Cork at 2:45.
   Three hours and 25 minutes later, it arrived in Dublin.
   At what time did it arrive in Dublin? _____

10. $\frac{3}{8}$ of the people in Greentown are children.
    If there are 738 children, how many people live in Greentown? _____

11. A rectangular garden is 28 metres long and 17 metres wide.
    What is the area of the garden? _____

12. Heather spent $\frac{5}{9}$ of her money buying a helmet.
    If she had €8·72 left, how much had she at first? _____

Score ☐ /12

6

3. Large Numbers

Mental Computation

1. $3200 + 500 =$ _____
2. $4730 + 60 =$ _____
3. $2864 + 4000 =$ _____
4. $2870 - 300 =$ _____
5. $5970 - 40 =$ _____
6. $8357 - 5000 =$ _____
7. $354 \times 10 =$ _____
8. $96 \times 100 =$ _____
9. $124 \times 100 =$ _____
10. $10\,000 + 9000 + 400 + 70 + 6 =$ _____
11. $20\,000 + 7000 + 300 + 80 + 9 =$ _____
12. $40\,000 + 800 + 6000 + 3 + 70 =$ _____
13. $500 + 7000 + 90 + 80\,000 + 6 =$ _____
14. $78\,540 - 6000 =$ _____
15. $81\,735 + 7000 =$ _____

Written Computation

1.
```
  23 574
+ 19 625
_____
```

2.
```
  34 187
+ 28 539
_____
```

3.
```
  42 658
+ 17 934
_____
```

4.
```
  37 693
+ 48 529
_____
```

5.
```
  14 367
  25 492
+ 34 683
_____
```

6.
```
  23 619
  27 184
+ 18 765
_____
```

7.
```
  28 726
  34 507
+ 15 789
_____
```

8.
```
  37 485
  29 328
+ 14 953
_____
```

9.
```
  54 362
  17 584
+ 21 768
_____
```

10.
```
  29 374
  38 569
+ 14 783
_____
```

11.
```
  38 479
  19 763
+ 25 497
_____
```

12.
```
  46 057
  13 928
+ 27 864
_____
```

13.
```
  47 325
- 18 432
_____
```

14.
```
  53 246
- 28 579
_____
```

15.
```
  64 237
- 38 542
_____
```

16.
```
  72 543
- 47 958
_____
```

17. 81 436	**18.** 92 364	**19.** 86 402	**20.** 73 005
− 53 628	− 68 519	− 57 315	− 29 276
————	————	————	————

Mental Problems

1. Write in figures
   thirty-seven thousand four hundred and eighty-five. _____

2. What is the value of the 6 in 63 524? _____

3.  There were 28 467 spectators at a football match one Sunday.
   The following Sunday, 7000 fewer attended.
   How many attended that Sunday? _____

4. There are 17 345 people living in Greentown.
   There are 2000 more than that living in Newtown.
   What is the population of Newtown? _____

5. Write in figures
   eighty-six thousand five hundred and nineteen. _____

6. Make the largest number possible using all these digits **7 2 3 9 5**. _____

7. Make the smallest number possible using all these digits **6 8 4 7 3**. _____

8.  29 467 people attended an open air concert in July.
   This was 8000 more than attended the previous year.
   How many people attended the previous year? _____

9. Which of these numbers is nearest to 80 000
   70 450, 85 000 **or** 76 000? _____

10. 32 560 people passed through an airport one Friday.
    6200 more than that passed through the following Friday.
    How many people passed through that Friday? _____

11. What number is 3020 greater than 56 740? _____

12. 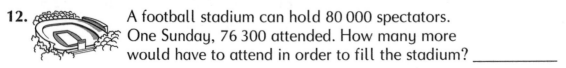 A football stadium can hold 80 000 spectators.
    One Sunday, 76 300 attended. How many more
    would have to attend in order to fill the stadium? _____

Written Problems

1. What is the sum of 18 236, 23 567 and 14 694? _____

2. What is the difference between 34 526 and 18 749? _____

3. There are 18 638 people living in Glenville.
   There are 5649 more than that living in Edenville.
   What is the population of Edenville? _____

4. One week, a newsagent sold 13 679 papers.
   The following week, 978 more papers were sold.
   How many papers were sold that week? _____

5. One Sunday, 24 526 spectators attended a football match.
   5768 fewer than that attended the next Sunday.
   How many attended that Sunday? _____

6. Find the sum of twenty-four thousand seven hundred and sixteen and
   thirty-eight thousand and ninety-seven. _____

7. By how much is 42 513 greater than the sum of 23 459 and 14 978? _____

8. 43 265 people attended a football match.
   19 678 of them were men and 14 897 were women.
   How many children attended the match? _____

9. What must be added to the sum of 19 582 and 23 465 to make 47 530? _____

10. A factory made 13 728 shirts one month.
    It made 4785 more shirts than that the next month.
    How many shirts were made during the two months? _____

11. A company sold 27 296 cars one year. It sold 5687 less cars the next year.
    How many cars were sold during the two years? _____

12. 3 5 2 8 7   Using all of these digits each time,
    subtract the smallest number that can be made
    from the largest number that can be made. _____

4. Multiplication

Mental Computation

1. $(8 \times 9) + 7 =$ _____
2. $(6 \times 7) + 9 =$ _____
3. $(9 \times 5) + 8 =$ _____
4. $(9 \times 6) - 5 =$ _____
5. $(7 \times 9) - 8 =$ _____
6. $(8 \times 8) - 6 =$ _____
7. $38 \times 10 =$ _____
8. $157 \times 10 =$ _____
9. $679 \times 10 =$ _____
10. $12 \times 20 =$ _____
11. $16 \times 20 =$ _____
12. $23 \times 20 =$ _____
13. $11 \times 30 =$ _____
14. $20 \times 30 =$ _____
15. $30 \times 30 =$ _____

Written Computation

1. $\begin{array}{r} 258 \\ \times\,23 \\ \hline \end{array}$
2. $\begin{array}{r} 379 \\ \times\,89 \\ \hline \end{array}$
3. $\begin{array}{r} 637 \\ \times\,59 \\ \hline \end{array}$
4. $\begin{array}{r} 49 \\ \times\,76 \\ \hline \end{array}$

5. $\begin{array}{r} 465 \\ \times\,48 \\ \hline \end{array}$
6. $\begin{array}{r} 743 \\ \times\,38 \\ \hline \end{array}$
7. $\begin{array}{r} 508 \\ \times\,78 \\ \hline \end{array}$
8. $\begin{array}{r} 879 \\ \times\,69 \\ \hline \end{array}$

9. $\begin{array}{r} 3417 \\ \times\,16 \\ \hline \end{array}$
10. $\begin{array}{r} 3526 \\ \times\,23 \\ \hline \end{array}$
11. $\begin{array}{r} 1269 \\ \times\,58 \\ \hline \end{array}$
12. $\begin{array}{r} 2358 \\ \times\,37 \\ \hline \end{array}$

13. $\begin{array}{r} 2347 \\ \times\,38 \\ \hline \end{array}$
14. $\begin{array}{r} 1489 \\ \times\,57 \\ \hline \end{array}$
15. $\begin{array}{r} 1259 \\ \times\,63 \\ \hline \end{array}$
16. $\begin{array}{r} 1273 \\ \times\,68 \\ \hline \end{array}$

17. $\begin{array}{r} 1634 \\ \times\,59 \\ \hline \end{array}$
18. $\begin{array}{r} 1039 \\ \times\,78 \\ \hline \end{array}$
19. $\begin{array}{r} 1263 \\ \times\,74 \\ \hline \end{array}$
20. $\begin{array}{r} 1347 \\ \times\,69 \\ \hline \end{array}$

Mental Problems

1.  There are 178 straws in a box.
How many straws are there in 10 boxes? _____

2.  There are 25 plums in a bag.
How many plums are there in 11 bags? _____

3. What must be added to 9 times 9 to make 100? _____

4. By how much is 150 greater than 10 times 12? _____

5.  There are 12 eggs on a tray.
How many eggs are there on 9 trays? _____

6.  There were 100 sweets in a bag.
When 8 children had each taken 9 sweets from the bag,
how many sweets were left? _____

7.  Pat had 60 balloons.
He gave 7 balloons to each of 6 children.
How many balloons had he left? _____

8. **12** James has 7 bags of apples and 9 loose apples.
How many apples has he altogether? _____

9.  **70 oranges** How many oranges altogether are there in 8 boxes? _____

10. What must be added to the product of 45 and 20 to make 1000? _____

11. **38 stamps** David bought 9 packets of stamps.
How many stamps less than 350 was that? _____

12. What is the difference between 17 times 236 and 27 times 236? _____

11

Written Problems

1. A newsagent sold 786 newspapers each week.
   How many newspapers did she sell in a year (52 weeks)? _____

2. What number is 28 times greater than 973? _____

3. A factory produces 647 mobile phones each day.
   How many phones will it produce in 39 days? _____

4. A cinema has seats for 278 people.
   What is the total number of people that may be seated
   for 26 showings of a film? _____

5. An aeroplane can carry 386 passengers.
   How many passengers can 29 aeroplanes carry? _____

6. A theatre can seat 248 patrons.
   How many patrons less than 10 000 attended 37 performances,
   if all the seats were occupied for each performance? _____

7. There are 278 pages in a book.
   How many pages less than 9000 are there in 28 such books? _7784_

8. A forester planted 36 rows of trees
   with 249 trees in each row.
   How many more trees must he plant
   to make a total of 10 000 trees? _1036_

9. Joe was asked to multiply 356 by 48.
   Instead he multiplied 356 by 84.
   By how much was his answer too big? _12816_

10. A chocolate factory produced 384 bars each day.
    How many bars less than 11 000 were produced
    during the month of February (28 days)? _258_

11. A fruit merchant has 78 boxes of oranges with 148 in each box
    and 52 boxes of apples with 148 in each box.
    How many more oranges than apples has he? _3848_

12. By how much is the product of 687 and 94 greater than 56 782? _1796_

5. 2-D Shapes

1. Name each of these 2-D shapes.
   (Choose from **pentagon, triangle, circle, rhombus, parallelogram, semi-circle, hexagon, octagon.**)

   (a) _____

   (b) _____

   (c) _____

   (d) _____

   (e) _____

   (f) _____

   (g) _____

   (h) _____

2. Complete these facts.

   (a) A rhombus is a _____ pulled out of shape.

   (b) A parallelogram is a _____ pulled out of shape.

   (c) A _____ has five straight sides.

   (d) A _____ has six straight sides.

   (e) An octagon has _____ straight sides.

3. Name each of these triangles.
   (Choose from **equilateral, isosceles** or **scalene.**)

   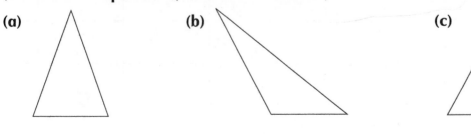

   (a) _____   **(b)** _____   **(c)** _____

4. Write **true** or **false** for each of these statements.　　　　**true / false**

   (a) A triangle with no sides equal is a scalene triangle.   ＿＿＿＿＿＿

   (b) A square has four axes of symmetry.   ＿＿＿＿＿＿

   (c) A rectangle has four axes of symmetry.   ＿＿＿＿＿＿

   (d) An equilateral triangle has three axes of symmetry.   ＿＿＿＿＿＿

   (e) A parallelogram has no axes of symmetry.   ＿＿＿＿＿＿

   (f) A rhombus has four axes of symmetry.   ＿＿＿＿＿＿

   (g) A four-sided figure with two sides parallel is called a trapezium.   ＿＿＿＿＿＿

   (h) A triangle with one right angle is called a right-angled triangle.   ＿＿＿＿＿＿

5. Complete this table about **2-D shapes**.

name of shape	number of sides	number of angles	number of right angles	number of acute angles	number of obtuse angles	number of axes of symmetry
rectangle			4			
rhombus			0	2		
parallelogram			0		2	0
square						
equilateral triangle					0	
regular pentagon			0			5
regular hexagon				0		
regular octagon						8

6. What shapes do you see in these tessellating pictures?

(a)    **(b)** 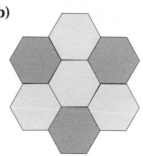   **(c)**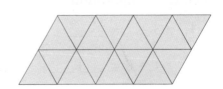

_____   _____   _____

7. Write **true** or **false** for each of these statements.   **true / false**

(a) Squares are good shapes for tessellating.   _____

(b) Circles are good shapes for tessellating.   _____

(c) Rectangles are good shapes for tessellating.   _____

(d) Equilateral triangles are good shapes for tessellating.   _____

8. Here is a picture of a tangram.
It is a **square** divided into **7 pieces**.
We can use some or all of the pieces
to make other shapes.

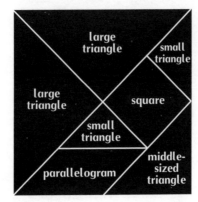

Make the following shapes using all of the pieces.

(a) rabbit   **(b)** cat   **(c)** swan

6. Division

Mental Computation

1. $63 \div 7 =$ _____   **2.** $32 \div 4 =$ _____   **3.** $48 \div 8 =$ _____

4. $51 \div 6 =$ ___R___   **5.** $71 \div 9 =$ ___R___   **6.** $39 \div 4 =$ ___R___

7. $90 \div 10 =$ _____   **8.** $300 \div 10 =$ _____   **9.** $180 \div 10 =$ _____

10. $165 \div 10 =$ ___R___   **11.** $248 \div 10 =$ ___R___   **12.** $367 \div 10 =$ ___R___

13. $160 \div 20 =$ _____   **14.** $240 \div 20 =$ _____   **15.** $380 \div 20 =$ _____

Written Computation (A)

1. $6 \overline{)937}$ **2.** $9 \overline{)647}$ **3.** $7 \overline{)873}$ **4.** $8 \overline{)967}$

5. $28 \overline{)237}$ **6.** $41 \overline{)294}$ **7.** $53 \overline{)387}$ **8.** $74 \overline{)568}$

9. $36 \overline{)852}$ **10.** $28 \overline{)675}$ **11.** $27 \overline{)846}$ **12.** $24 \overline{)739}$

13. $37 \overline{)935}$ **14.** $29 \overline{)948}$ **15.** $34 \overline{)837}$ **16.** $45 \overline{)978}$

17. $57 \overline{)792}$ **18.** $43 \overline{)687}$ **19.** $38 \overline{)895}$ **20.** $56 \overline{)906}$

Written Computation (B)

Do these in your copybook. Before doing each, **estimate** the answer by **rounding** the **3-digit number** to the **nearest hundred** and the **2-digit number** to the **nearest ten**.

Example $674 \div 43 = \boxed{?}$

Estimate $\Rightarrow 700 \div 40$

$\Rightarrow 70 \text{ tens} \div 4 \text{ tens}$

$\Rightarrow 70 \div 4$

$\Rightarrow 17$

My estimate is **17**.

```
        15
43 ) 674
     43
     244
     215
      29
```

Answer $\boxed{15 \text{ R } 29}$

1. $378 \div 23 = \boxed{?}$

Estimate _____

Answer _____

2. $429 \div 26 = \boxed{?}$

_____

_____

3. $527 \div 34 = \boxed{?}$

_____

_____

4. $569 \div 48 = \boxed{?}$

Estimate _____

Answer _____

5. $628 \div 47 = \boxed{?}$

_____

_____

6. $736 \div 54 = \boxed{?}$

_____

_____

7. $863 \div 48 = \boxed{?}$

Estimate _____

Answer _____

8. $758 \div 36 = \boxed{?}$

_____

_____

9. $638 \div 29 = \boxed{?}$

_____

_____

10. $924 \div 41 = \boxed{?}$

Estimate _____

Answer _____

11. $867 \div 39 = \boxed{?}$

_____

_____

12. $793 \div 32 = \boxed{?}$

_____

_____

13. $597 \div 19 = \boxed{?}$

Estimate _____

Answer _____

14. $684 \div 27 = \boxed{?}$

_____

_____

15. $829 \div 35 = \boxed{?}$

_____

_____

16. $726 \div 18 = \boxed{?}$

Estimate _____

Answer _____

17. $873 \div 21 = \boxed{?}$

_____

_____

18. $791 \div 58 = \boxed{?}$

_____

_____

Written Problems

(Estimate each answer before doing the problem.)

1. How many bags, each holding 16 apples, can be filled from a box that holds 144 apples? _____

2. It takes 26 chocolates to fill a box. How many boxes can be filled from 390 chocolates? _____

3. A bus can carry 46 passengers. How many buses are needed to carry 828 passengers? _____

4. There are 34 biscuits in each packet. How many packets can be filled from 952 biscuits? _____

5. How many bags, each holding 18 plums, can be filled from a box containing 455 and how many plums are left? _____R_____

6. How many 48-page copybooks can be made from 930 pages and how many pages are left? _____R_____

7. A farmer sows cabbages with 35 cabbages in each row. How many rows can he sow with 867 cabbages and how many cabbages will he have left? _____R_____

8. Milk is packed in cartons of 27. How many packs can be made from 990 cartons and how many cartons are left? _____R_____

9. How many boxes of 36 crayons can be made from 695 crayons and how many crayons are left? _____R_____

10. How many times can I take 56 from 973 and what will be left? _____R_____

11. There were 451 green apples and 395 red apples in a box. They were packed into bags of 18. How many bags were filled? _____

12. There were 621 oranges in a box. 13 of them were bad and the rest were packed into bags of 16. How many bags were filled? _____

7. Fractions 1

Mental Computation (A)

one unit			
$\frac{1}{2}$		$\frac{1}{2}$	
$\frac{1}{4}$	$\frac{1}{4}$	$\frac{1}{4}$	$\frac{1}{4}$
$\frac{1}{8}$ $\frac{1}{8}$ $\frac{1}{8}$ $\frac{1}{8}$		$\frac{1}{8}$ $\frac{1}{8}$ $\frac{1}{8}$ $\frac{1}{8}$	

one unit		
$\frac{1}{3}$	$\frac{1}{3}$	$\frac{1}{3}$
$\frac{1}{6}$ $\frac{1}{6}$	$\frac{1}{6}$ $\frac{1}{6}$	$\frac{1}{6}$ $\frac{1}{6}$
$\frac{1}{12}$ $\frac{1}{12}$ $\frac{1}{12}$ $\frac{1}{12}$	$\frac{1}{12}$ $\frac{1}{12}$ $\frac{1}{12}$ $\frac{1}{12}$	$\frac{1}{12}$ $\frac{1}{12}$ $\frac{1}{12}$ $\frac{1}{12}$

1. $\frac{1}{2} = \frac{}{8}$

2. $\frac{3}{4} = \frac{}{8}$

3. $\frac{1}{3} = \frac{}{12}$

4. $\frac{2}{3} = \frac{}{6}$

5. $\frac{2}{3} = \frac{}{12}$

6. $\frac{1}{6} = \frac{}{12}$

7. $\frac{5}{6} = \frac{}{12}$

8. $\frac{1}{2} = \frac{}{12}$

9. $\frac{1}{2} = \frac{}{10}$

10. $\frac{1}{4} = \frac{}{12}$

11. $\frac{1}{3} = \frac{}{9}$

12. $\frac{2}{3} = \frac{}{9}$

13. $\frac{1}{5} = \frac{}{10}$

14. $\frac{3}{5} = \frac{}{10}$

15. $\frac{4}{5} = \frac{}{10}$

16. $\frac{3}{4} = \frac{}{12}$

Mental Computation (B)

Write these **improper fractions** as **mixed numbers**.

1. $\frac{3}{2} = $ _____

2. $\frac{11}{8} = $ _____

3. $\frac{13}{5} = $ _____

4. $\frac{17}{9} = $ _____

5. $\frac{13}{4} = $ _____

6. $\frac{37}{10} = $ _____

7. $\frac{23}{6} = $ _____

8. $\frac{35}{12} = $ _____

9. $\frac{18}{5} = $ _____

10. $\frac{37}{8} = $ _____

11. $\frac{43}{9} = $ _____

12. $\frac{26}{3} = $ _____

Write these **mixed numbers** as **improper fractions**.

13. $1\frac{3}{4} = $ _____

14. $1\frac{7}{9} = $ _____

15. $2\frac{2}{3} = $ _____

16. $2\frac{7}{8} = $ _____

17. $2\frac{4}{5} = $ _____

18. $2\frac{8}{9} = $ _____

19. $3\frac{1}{6} = $ _____

20. $7\frac{1}{2} = $ _____

21. $6\frac{9}{10} = $ _____

22. $2\frac{7}{12} = $ _____

23. $5\frac{7}{8} = $ _____

24. $9\frac{3}{4} = $ _____

25. $7\frac{5}{6} = $ _____

26. $8\frac{3}{5} = $ _____

27. $6\frac{7}{9} = $ _____

28. $4\frac{5}{7} = $ _____

Written Computation (A)

1. $\frac{1}{2} + \frac{1}{4} =$ _____

2. $\frac{1}{4} + \frac{3}{8} =$ _____

3. $\frac{1}{6} + \frac{2}{3} =$ _____

4. $\frac{1}{2} + \frac{1}{6} =$ _____

5. $\frac{5}{6} + \frac{1}{3} =$ _____

6. $\frac{3}{4} + \frac{3}{8} =$ _____

7. $\frac{1}{4} + \frac{5}{12} =$ _____

8. $\frac{4}{9} + \frac{2}{3} =$ _____

9. $\frac{7}{10} + \frac{4}{5} =$ _____

10. $\frac{5}{6} + \frac{7}{12} =$ _____

11. $\frac{3}{4} + \frac{5}{12} =$ _____

12. $\frac{2}{3} + \frac{11}{12} =$ _____

13. $\frac{8}{9} + \frac{2}{3} =$ _____

14. $\frac{11}{12} + \frac{5}{6} =$ _____

15. $\frac{4}{5} + \frac{9}{10} =$ _____

16. $\frac{3}{4} + \frac{5}{8} =$ _____

17. $\frac{11}{12} + \frac{1}{2} =$ _____

18. $\frac{7}{8} + \frac{3}{4} =$ _____

19. $\frac{5}{6} + \frac{5}{12} =$ _____

20. $\frac{7}{12} + \frac{3}{4} =$ _____

21. $\frac{2}{3} + \frac{5}{12} =$ _____

Written Computation (B)

1. $\frac{1}{2} - \frac{1}{4} =$ _____

2. $\frac{7}{8} - \frac{1}{4} =$ _____

3. $\frac{5}{9} - \frac{1}{3} =$ _____

4. $\frac{3}{4} - \frac{5}{8} =$ _____

5. $\frac{5}{6} - \frac{5}{12} =$ _____

6. $\frac{2}{3} - \frac{4}{9} =$ _____

7. $\frac{11}{12} - \frac{1}{6} =$ _____

8. $\frac{3}{4} - \frac{3}{8} =$ _____

9. $\frac{9}{10} - \frac{3}{5} =$ _____

10. $\frac{7}{12} - \frac{1}{3} =$ _____

11. $\frac{11}{12} - \frac{1}{4} =$ _____

12. $\frac{8}{9} - \frac{2}{3} =$ _____

13. $\frac{7}{10} - \frac{2}{5} =$ _____

14. $\frac{9}{10} - \frac{1}{2} =$ _____

15. $\frac{4}{5} - \frac{3}{10} =$ _____

16. $\frac{11}{12} - \frac{1}{2} =$ _____

17. $\frac{7}{12} - \frac{1}{6} =$ _____

18. $\frac{11}{12} - \frac{2}{3} =$ _____

19. $\frac{1}{2} - \frac{3}{10} =$ _____

20. $\frac{11}{12} - \frac{3}{4} =$ _____

21. $\frac{2}{3} - \frac{2}{9} =$ _____

Mental Problems

1. Peter ate five of his twelve sweets.
   What fraction of the sweets did he eat? _____

2. Seven of the ten apples in a bag are green.
   What fraction of the apples is green? _____

3. Linda has €9 and Leo has €6.
   Express Leo's money as a fraction of Linda's money. _____

4. There were 12 flowers in a jar. Ann took 3 of them.
   What fraction of the flowers was left in the jar? _____

5. A farmer had 30 sheep. She sold $\frac{2}{3}$ of them.
   How many sheep did she sell? _____

6. $\frac{5}{9}$ of the pupils in a school are girls.
   If 90 pupils attend the school, how many are girls? _____

7. Elaine has saved $\frac{5}{8}$ of the cost of a bicycle.
   If the bicycle costs €72, how much has she saved? _____

8. $\frac{2}{3}$ of the animals on a farm are sheep.
   If there are 18 sheep, how many animals are there
   on the farm altogether? _____

9. Jason had a bar of chocolate.
   He ate $\frac{7}{12}$ of it.
   What fraction of the chocolate was left? _____

10. $\frac{5}{8}$ of the apples in a box are green.
    If there are 40 green apples,
    how many apples altogether are there? _____

11. How many quarter bars can I get from $2\frac{3}{4}$ bars of chocolate? _____

12. Jim has read $\frac{7}{9}$ of the 72 pages in a book.
    How many pages has he still to read? _____

8. Fractions 2

Mental Computation

1. Start at **0** and count in **thirds**.
   (Use **mixed numbers** when greater than a unit.)

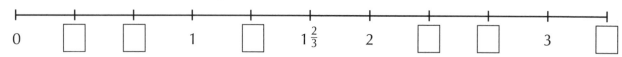

2. Start at **0** and count in **quarters**.
   (Use **mixed numbers** where necessary.)

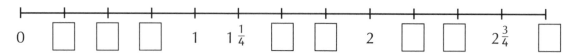

3. Start at **0** and count in **twelfths**.

> Use **lowest terms** where possible.
> Remember $\frac{2}{12} = \frac{1}{6}$, $\frac{4}{12} = \frac{1}{3}$ etc.

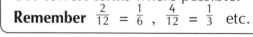

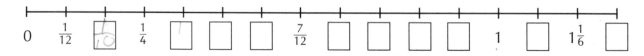

Write these **improper fractions** as **mixed numbers**.

4. $\frac{17}{2}$ = _____

5. $\frac{29}{4}$ = _____

6. $\frac{53}{6}$ = _____

7. $\frac{41}{7}$ = _____

8. $\frac{77}{8}$ = _____

9. $\frac{67}{9}$ = _____

10. $\frac{43}{12}$ = _____

11. $\frac{49}{5}$ = _____

Write these **mixed numbers** as **improper fractions**.

12. $3\frac{3}{4}$ = _____

13. $6\frac{2}{3}$ = _____

14. $7\frac{4}{5}$ = _____

15. $8\frac{3}{4}$ = _____

16. $3\frac{6}{7}$ = _____

17. $9\frac{5}{6}$ = _____

18. $8\frac{7}{10}$ = _____

19. $7\frac{5}{9}$ = _____

20. $4\frac{5}{12}$ = _____

21. $8\frac{7}{9}$ = _____

22. $3\frac{7}{12}$ = _____

23. $9\frac{7}{8}$ = _____

Written Computation (A)

1. $2\frac{1}{2} + 1\frac{1}{4} =$ _____

2. $1\frac{1}{2} + 2\frac{3}{8} =$ _____

3. $2\frac{1}{6} + 3\frac{1}{3} =$ _____

4. $3\frac{1}{8} + 2\frac{3}{4} =$ _____

5. $2\frac{1}{3} + 3\frac{4}{9} =$ _____

6. $2\frac{3}{5} + 4\frac{3}{10} =$ _____

7. $3\frac{1}{2} + 2\frac{1}{6} =$ _____

8. $2\frac{3}{10} + 3\frac{1}{2} =$ _____

9. $3\frac{1}{4} + 1\frac{1}{12} =$ _____

10. $3\frac{2}{5} + 1\frac{7}{10} =$ _____

11. $2\frac{1}{2} + 3\frac{5}{6} =$ _____

12. $3\frac{11}{12} + 2\frac{1}{4} =$ _____

13. $4\frac{1}{6} - 1\frac{1}{12} =$ _____

14. $3\frac{7}{8} - 2\frac{1}{2} =$ _____

15. $5\frac{3}{5} - 2\frac{3}{10} =$ _____

16. $4\frac{7}{10} - 1\frac{1}{5} =$ _____

17. $5\frac{1}{2} - 3\frac{1}{6} =$ _____

18. $4\frac{3}{4} - 2\frac{7}{12} =$ _____

19. $6\frac{5}{8} - 3\frac{3}{4} =$ _____

20. $4\frac{5}{6} - 1\frac{11}{12} =$ _____

21. $5\frac{1}{4} - 2\frac{3}{8} =$ _____

22. $5\frac{1}{3} - 2\frac{5}{6} =$ _____

23. $7\frac{1}{4} - 2\frac{7}{12} =$ _____

24. $4\frac{5}{12} - 2\frac{3}{4} =$ _____

Written Computation (B)

(Write answers as **mixed numbers** in lowest terms where possible.)

1. $\frac{1}{3} \times 2 =$ _____

2. $\frac{1}{4} \times 3 =$ _____

3. $5 \times \frac{1}{6} =$ _____

4. $\frac{1}{6} \times 3 =$ _____

5. $\frac{1}{8} \times 4 =$ _____

6. $6 \times \frac{1}{8} =$ _____

7. $\frac{1}{10} \times 8 =$ _____

8. $9 \times \frac{1}{12} =$ _____

9. $\frac{1}{9} \times 6 =$ _____

10. $\frac{1}{3} \times 5 =$ _____

11. $\frac{1}{4} \times 9 =$ _____

12. $11 \times \frac{1}{5} =$ _____

13. $\frac{3}{4} \times 2 =$ _____

14. $\frac{2}{3} \times 5 =$ _____

15. $6 \times \frac{3}{4} =$ _____

16. $\frac{2}{5} \times 7 =$ _____

17. $\frac{5}{6} \times 3 =$ _____

18. $\frac{5}{9} \times 6 =$ _____

19. $\frac{5}{12} \times 4 =$ _____

20. $\frac{7}{8} \times 4 =$ _____

21. $\frac{9}{10} \times 5 =$ _____

Mental Problems

1. Paul ate 8 of the 12 bars.
What fraction of the bars did he eat? _____

2. 6 of the 16 oranges in a bag were removed.
What fraction of the oranges was removed? _____

3. 10 of the 12 children in a group like football.
What fraction of the group likes football? _____

4. $\frac{3}{4}$ of a number is 27. What is the number? _____

5. Kathy has read $\frac{5}{12}$ of her book.
What fraction of the book has she still to read? _____

6. $\frac{5}{8}$ of the apples in a box are green.
If there are 45 green apples,
how many apples are there in the box altogether? _____

7. Mam has 7 bars of chocolate.
To how many children can she give a half bar? _____

8. Ben spent $\frac{4}{5}$ of his money buying a helmet.
If the helmet cost €20, how much had Ben at first? _____

9. 4 children each ate $\frac{3}{4}$ of a pizza.
How many pizzas altogether did they eat? _____

10. 6 children each drank $\frac{2}{3}$ of a bottle of orange.
How many bottles of orange altogether did they drink? _____

11. How many quarter bars can I get from $3\frac{3}{4}$ bars of chocolate? _____

12. John has read $\frac{5}{9}$ of the 45 pages in an annual.
How many pages has he still to read? _____

24

Written Problems

1.  Alan ate $\frac{1}{4}$ of a pizza and Ann ate $\frac{3}{8}$ of it.
   What fraction of the pizza did they eat between them? _____

2.  Andrew read $\frac{1}{2}$ of his book in the morning and $\frac{3}{8}$ of it in the afternoon.
   What fraction of the book had he then read? _____

3.  Eileen spent $\frac{1}{6}$ of her money on shoes and $\frac{2}{3}$ of it on clothes.
   What fraction of her money had she then spent? _____

4.  Mark ate $\frac{3}{4}$ of a bar of chocolate before lunch and $1\frac{1}{2}$ bars after lunch.
   How much chocolate did he eat altogether? _____

5.  Joan has $1\frac{3}{4}$ boxes of sweets and Joe has $2\frac{3}{8}$ boxes.
   How many boxes of sweets have they between them? _____

6.  A pizza shop sold $3\frac{2}{3}$ pizzas for breakfast and $4\frac{5}{6}$ pizzas for lunch.
   How many pizzas altogether were sold? _____

7.  Tom had $3\frac{1}{4}$ bars of chocolate. He ate $1\frac{5}{8}$ bars.
   How much chocolate had he left? _____

8.  A tradesman had $5\frac{4}{9}$ rolls of wallpaper. He used $2\frac{2}{3}$ rolls.
   How many rolls of wallpaper had he left? _____

9. By how much is $7\frac{5}{12}$ greater than $4\frac{3}{4}$? _____

10.  5 children each ate $\frac{3}{4}$ of a bar of chocolate.
    How many bars did they eat altogether? _____

11.  7 children each drank $\frac{5}{8}$ of a bottle of water.
    How many bottles of water altogether did they drink? _____

12. Avril has read $\frac{4}{9}$ of the 108 pages in an annual.
    How many pages has she still to read? _____

9. Test Yourself 1

Mental Computation

1. $2300 + 500 =$ _____

2. $3865 + 4000 =$ _____

3. $6510 + 80 =$ _____

4. $5728 - 400 =$ _____

5. $5386 - 70 =$ _____

6. $9462 - 5000 =$ _____

7. $287 \times 10 =$ _____

8. $17 \times 20 =$ _____

9. $34 \times 20 =$ _____

10. $59 \div 6 =$ ____R____

11. $97 \div 10 =$ ____R____

12. $180 \div 20 =$ _____

13. $\frac{2}{3} = \frac{}{12}$

14. $\frac{1}{4} + \frac{1}{8} =$ _____

15. $4 \times \frac{2}{9} =$ _____

Score [ ] /15

Written Computation

1.
$$\begin{array}{r} 13\,589 \\ 24\,637 \\ + 35\,026 \\ \hline \end{array}$$

2.
$$\begin{array}{r} 24\,639 \\ 18\,793 \\ + 26\,851 \\ \hline \end{array}$$

3.
$$\begin{array}{r} 32\,506 \\ 17\,928 \\ + 25\,837 \\ \hline \end{array}$$

4.
$$\begin{array}{r} 24\,671 \\ 35\,864 \\ + 19\,735 \\ \hline \end{array}$$

5.
$$\begin{array}{r} 48\,352 \\ - 17\,684 \\ \hline \end{array}$$

6.
$$\begin{array}{r} 54\,263 \\ - 28\,795 \\ \hline \end{array}$$

7.
$$\begin{array}{r} 62\,530 \\ - 29\,653 \\ \hline \end{array}$$

8.
$$\begin{array}{r} 71\,004 \\ - 53\,279 \\ \hline \end{array}$$

9.
$$\begin{array}{r} 2136 \\ \times 28 \\ \hline \end{array}$$

10.
$$\begin{array}{r} 1958 \\ \times 37 \\ \hline \end{array}$$

11.
$$\begin{array}{r} 1247 \\ \times 69 \\ \hline \end{array}$$

12.
$$\begin{array}{r} 1026 \\ \times 78 \\ \hline \end{array}$$

13. $36\overline{)932}$

14. $43\overline{)795}$

15. $57\overline{)978}$

16. $63\overline{)908}$

17. $28\overline{)927}$

18. $39\overline{)845}$

19. $19\overline{)704}$

20. $24\overline{)835}$

21. $2\frac{1}{4} + 1\frac{3}{8} =$ _____

22. $1\frac{1}{2} + 4\frac{7}{10} =$ _____

23. $3\frac{3}{4} + 2\frac{5}{12} =$ _____

24. $5\frac{7}{10} - 1\frac{1}{5} =$ _____

25. $6\frac{1}{4} - 2\frac{7}{12} =$ _____

26. $\frac{4}{9} \times 6 =$ _____

Score [ ] /26

Mental Problems

1. Write in figures
   forty-nine thousand six hundred and thirteen. _____

2. What is the value of the 7 in 78 369? _____

3. There are 14 628 people living in Abbeyville.
   There are 3000 more than that living in Poolesville.
   What is the population of Poolesville? _____

4. 28 593 people attended an open air concert in June.
   This was 7000 more than attended the previous year.
   How many attended the previous year? _____

5. **60** 🍎 How many apples altogether are there in nine boxes? _____

6. What must be added to the product of 35 and 20 to make 750? _____

7. By how much is 29 times 178 greater than 19 times 178? _____

8. **88** oranges — How many bags of 9 oranges can be filled from this
   box of oranges and how many oranges will be left? _____R_____

9. A minibus can carry 12 people.
   How many minibuses are needed to carry 80 people? _____

10. $\frac{3}{5}$ of the animals on a farm are sheep.
    If there are 30 sheep,
    how many animals are there on the farm altogether? _____

11. 5 children each ate $\frac{3}{4}$ of a pizza.
    How many pizzas altogether did they eat? _____

12. 4 children each drank $\frac{2}{3}$ of a bottle of water.
    How many bottles of water altogether did they drink? _____

Score [/12]

Written Problems

1. What is the sum of 17 268, 23 570 and 16 895? _____

2. One Sunday, 23 256 people attended a football match. 4378 fewer than that attended the next Sunday. How many attended that Sunday? _____

3. By how much is 52 463 greater than the sum of 24 375 and 19 604? _____

4. What number is 26 times greater than 938? _____

5. An aeroplane can carry 378 passengers. How many passengers will 24 aeroplanes carry? _____

6. By how much is the product of 596 and 78 less than 50 000? _____

7. A bus can carry 56 passengers. How many buses are needed to carry 952 passengers? _____

8. How many boxes of 28 crayons can be made from 750 crayons and how many crayons are left? _____R_____

9. There were 395 red apples and 533 green apples in a box. The apples were packed into bags of 16. How many bags were filled? _____

10. Jim has $2\frac{3}{4}$ boxes of sweets and Jane has $3\frac{5}{8}$ boxes. How many boxes of sweets have they between them? _____

11. A decorator had $7\frac{2}{9}$ rolls of wallpaper. He used $4\frac{2}{3}$ rolls. How many rolls of wallpaper had he left? _____

12. 9 children each drank $\frac{5}{8}$ of a bottle of water. How many bottles of water did they drink altogether? _____

Score [/12]

10. Decimals 1

Activity Page

What **decimal fraction** of each shape is shaded?

1.

———————

2.

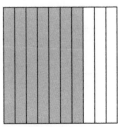

———————

3.

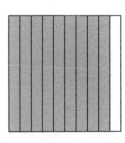

———————

4.

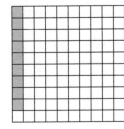

———————

5.

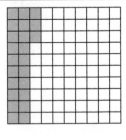

———————

6.

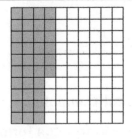

———————

7. Shade 0·6 of this shape.

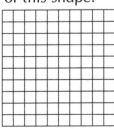

8. Shade 0·13 of this shape.

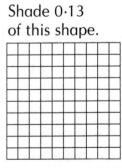

q. Shade 0·47 of this shape.

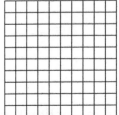

Write the missing decimals on the **number line**.

10.

0   0·1   0·2   [ ] [ ] [ ] [ ] [ ] [ ] [ ]   1   1·1   [ ]

11.

4   4·1   [ ]   4·3   [ ] [ ]   4·6   [ ] [ ] [ ]   5   [ ] [ ]

12.

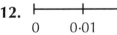

0   0·01   0·02   [ ] [ ] [ ]   0·06   [ ] [ ] [ ] [ ]

29

Mental Computation (A)

Write in **decimal form**.

1. $1\frac{1}{10} =$ _____

2. $1\frac{9}{10} =$ _____

3. $2\frac{3}{10} =$ _____

4. $4\frac{7}{10} =$ _____

5. $1\frac{1}{100} =$ _____

6. $2\frac{3}{100} =$ _____

7. $4\frac{7}{100} =$ _____

8. $7\frac{9}{100} =$ _____

9. $1\frac{13}{100} =$ _____

10. $3\frac{27}{100} =$ _____

11. $5\frac{49}{100} =$ _____

12. $6\frac{87}{100} =$ _____

13. $1 + \frac{7}{10} + \frac{9}{100} =$ _____

14. $2 + \frac{3}{10} + \frac{8}{100} =$ _____

15. $3 + \frac{1}{10} + \frac{7}{100} =$ _____

16. $6 + \frac{9}{10} + \frac{3}{100} =$ _____

17. $\frac{17}{10} =$ _____

18. $\frac{49}{10} =$ _____

19. $\frac{137}{100} =$ _____

20. $\frac{209}{100} =$ _____

Mental Computation (B)

Write in **fraction form**.

1. $0.7 =$ _____

2. $0.9 =$ _____

3. $1.3 =$ _____

4. $2.1 =$ _____

5. $0.03 =$ _____

6. $1.07 =$ _____

7. $3.09 =$ _____

8. $5.03 =$ _____

9. $0.17 =$ _____

10. $0.23 =$ _____

11. $0.49 =$ _____

12. $0.83 =$ _____

13. $2.19 =$ _____

14. $3.47 =$ _____

15. $4.23 =$ _____

16. $8.67 =$ _____

Write in **fraction form** the value of each **underlined** digit.

17. $3.\underline{7}5$ ☐

18. $4.2\underline{9}$ ☐

19. $36.\underline{3}1$ ☐

20. $18.6\underline{4}$ ☐

Written Computation (A)

1.
```
   23·67
   19·49
+ 34·85
───────
```

2.
```
   46·93
   28·67
+ 13·38
───────
```

3.
```
   29·64
   17·09
+ 26·78
───────
```

4.
```
   32·69
   18·75
+ 29·63
───────
```

5.	6.	7.	8.
76·24 − 38·59	80·27 − 29·65	90·00 − 67·43	70·05 − 23·58

9.	10.	11.	12.
23·57 × 6	34·82 × 7	56·49 × 5	72·68 × 8

13. $4\,|\,75{\cdot}6$ **14.** $5\,|\,94{\cdot}5$ **15.** $6\,|\,38{\cdot}4$ **16.** $8\,|\,93{\cdot}6$

17. $3\,|\,7{\cdot}35$ **18.** $7\,|\,9{\cdot}66$ **19.** $9\,|\,7{\cdot}92$ **20.** $6\,|\,8{\cdot}34$

Written Computation (B)

(Before doing these, write in **decimal form** first.)

1. $23\frac{7}{10} \Rightarrow$ ____
    $19\frac{13}{100} \Rightarrow$ ____
    $+\ 34\frac{39}{100} \Rightarrow$ ____

2. $16\frac{9}{10} \Rightarrow$ ____
    $27\frac{43}{100} \Rightarrow$ ____
    $+\ 38\frac{51}{100} \Rightarrow$ ____

3. $29\frac{17}{100} \Rightarrow$ ____
    $32\frac{8}{10} \Rightarrow$ ____
    $+16\frac{83}{100} \Rightarrow$ ____

4. $36\frac{29}{100} \Rightarrow$ ____
    $8\frac{47}{100} \Rightarrow$ ____
    $+\ 29\frac{4}{10} \Rightarrow$ ____

5. $27\frac{63}{100} \Rightarrow$ ____
    $38\frac{79}{100} \Rightarrow$ ____
    $+\ 9\frac{3}{100} \Rightarrow$ ____

6. $3\frac{9}{10} \Rightarrow$ ____
    $28\frac{7}{100} \Rightarrow$ ____
    $+\ 45\frac{89}{100} \Rightarrow$ ____

Mental Problems

1. A farmer had 60 sheep. She sold 0·3 of them.
How many sheep did she sell? _____

2. I had 70 stamps. I gave 0·6 of them to my friends.
How many stamps did I give to my friends? _____

3. There are 80 children in a school.
One day, 0·1 of them were absent.
How many children were present? _____

4. There were 12 apples in a bag.
Six of them were red.
What decimal fraction of them was red? _____

5. In a test, Derek got 87 marks out of 100.
Write his score in decimal form. _____

6. There are 100 children in a club. 93 of them like football.
What decimal fraction of them like football? _____

7. In a box of 100 oranges, there were 7 bad oranges.
What decimal fraction of the box of oranges was bad? _____

8. What do I get when I add 9 hundredths to 3·65? _____

9. 0·4 of a box of sweets costs 60c.
How much should a full box cost? _____

10. Mark thought of the number 3·72.
Mary thought of a number 5 hundredths less than that.
What number did Mary think of? _____

11. Having spent 0·8 of her money, Laura had €24 left.
How much had she at first? _____

12. Having sold 0·7 of his cows, a farmer had 27 cows left.
How many cows had the farmer at first? _____

Written Problems

1. Find the sum of 14·78, 9·65 and 28·9. _____

2. Richard thought of the number 37·43. Rachel thought of the number 56·3. What was the difference between the two numbers? _____

3. 0·7 of the trees in a forest are pine trees. If there are 686 pine trees, how many trees are there in the forest altogether? _____

4. There are 290 children in a school. 0·4 of them are boys. How many boys attend the school? _____

5. Donna spent 0·9 of her money and has €9·48 left. How much money had she at first? _____

6. There are 970 people living in Ashwood. 0·6 of them are adults. How many children live in Ashwood? _____

7. A farmer sold 0·3 of his animals and had 266 animals left. How many animals had the farmer at first? _____

8. Having completed 0·8 of a race, a cyclist still had 26km to go. What was the length of the race? _____

9. By how much is the 7 in 76·03 greater than the 7 in 58·47? _____

10. Elaine has read 0·4 of her book. If she still has 138 pages to read, how many pages are there in the book altogether? _____

11. Jim has €29·70. Joe has 0·8 of that amount. How much money have they between them? _____

12. 0·3 of Ellen's money is €8·37. What is 0·5 of her money? _____

11. Decimals 2

Mental Computation (A)

Write as **decimals**.

1. $\frac{1}{1000}$ = _____
2. $\frac{7}{1000}$ = _____
3. $\frac{9}{1000}$ = _____
4. $\frac{3}{1000}$ = _____

5. $\frac{13}{1000}$ = _____
6. $\frac{29}{1000}$ = _____
7. $\frac{37}{1000}$ = _____
8. $\frac{41}{1000}$ = _____

9. $\frac{63}{1000}$ = _____
10. $\frac{79}{1000}$ = _____
11. $\frac{87}{1000}$ = _____
12. $\frac{93}{1000}$ = _____

13. $\frac{127}{1000}$ = _____
14. $\frac{173}{1000}$ = _____
15. $\frac{189}{1000}$ = _____
16. $\frac{197}{1000}$ = _____

17. $\frac{269}{1000}$ = _____
18. $\frac{341}{1000}$ = _____
19. $\frac{463}{1000}$ = _____
20. $\frac{729}{1000}$ = _____

Mental Computation (B)

Write as **fractions**.

1. 0.004 = _____
2. 0.008 = _____
3. 0.019 = _____
4. 0.048 = _____

5. 0.076 = _____
6. 0.139 = _____
7. 0.287 = _____
8. 0.639 = _____

Write in **fraction form**.

9. 1.009 = _____
10. 1.038 = _____
11. 2.079 = _____
12. 4.083 = _____

13. 2.137 = _____
14. 3.259 = _____
15. 6.417 = _____
16. 8.763 = _____

Write each answer in **decimal form**.

17. $3 + \frac{7}{10} + \frac{9}{100} + \frac{1}{1000}$ = _____
18. $4 + \frac{3}{10} + \frac{8}{100} + \frac{4}{1000}$ = _____

19. $5 + \frac{8}{10} + \frac{7}{1000}$ = _____
20. $8 + \frac{3}{100} + \frac{9}{1000}$ = _____

Write in **fraction form** the value of each **underlined** digit.

21. $2.36\underline{7}$ [ ]
22. $1.4\underline{3}5$ [ ]
23. $3.64\underline{9}$ [ ]
24. $5.00\underline{8}$ [ ]

Written Computation (A)

1.
```
  3·762
  4·875
+ 1·239
───────
```

2.
```
  2·834
  3·971
+ 6·483
───────
```

3.
```
  4·896
  3·705
+ 7·638
───────
```

4.
```
  5·376
  9·287
+ 8·639
───────
```

5.
```
  28·347
  19·598
+ 26·729
────────
```

6.
```
  34·234
  27·537
+ 13·649
────────
```

7.
```
  26·409
  38·927
+ 15·683
────────
```

8.
```
  18·769
  35·376
+ 27·698
────────
```

9.
```
  58·724
- 35·697
────────
```

10.
```
  72·493
- 29·527
────────
```

11.
```
  67·345
- 48·679
────────
```

12.
```
  90·246
- 54·517
────────
```

13.
```
  3·485
  ×   7
───────
```

14.
```
  6·597
  ×   8
───────
```

15.
```
  9·283
  ×   6
───────
```

16.
```
  7·658
  ×   9
───────
```

17. 8⟌0·976

18. 7⟌0·833

19. 6⟌0·954

20. 4⟌0·956

Written Computation (B)

(Before doing these, write in **decimal form** first.)

1.
$4\frac{19}{100} \Rightarrow$

$\frac{37}{1000} \Rightarrow$

$+ 2\frac{153}{1000} \Rightarrow$

2.
$2\frac{329}{1000} \Rightarrow$

$4\frac{91}{100} \Rightarrow$

$+ 1\frac{47}{1000} \Rightarrow$

3.
$3\frac{57}{100} \Rightarrow$

$2\frac{631}{1000} \Rightarrow$

$+ 2\frac{79}{1000} \Rightarrow$

4. $4\frac{7}{10} \Rightarrow$ _____

$\frac{569}{1000} \Rightarrow$ _____

$+\ 3\frac{9}{100} \Rightarrow$ _____

_____ _____

5. $2\frac{89}{1000} \Rightarrow$ _____

$3\frac{7}{1000} \Rightarrow$ _____

$+\ 1\frac{3}{10} \Rightarrow$ _____

_____ _____

6. $2\frac{27}{100} \Rightarrow$ _____

$1\frac{89}{1000} \Rightarrow$ _____

$+\ \frac{853}{1000} \Rightarrow$ _____

_____ _____

Mental Problems

1.  There are 100 pupils in a school. 0·53 of them are girls. What decimal fraction of the pupils are boys? _____

2.  Jason had 100 stamps. He gave 0·28 of them to his friends. What decimal fraction of the stamps had he left? _____

3.  There were a thousand marbles in a box. The shopkeeper sold 357 of them. What decimal fraction of the marbles did she sell? _____

4.  When the athletes had completed 875m of a 1000 metre race, what decimal fraction of the race had they then completed? _____

5. 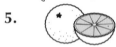 In a container of 1000, there were 37 bad oranges. What decimal fraction of the container of oranges was bad? _____

6. What do I get when I add 7 thousandths to 0·251? _____

7.  Joan thought of the number 3·462. Joe thought of a number 5 thousandths less than that. What number did Joe think of? _____

8.  0·6 of a box of sweets cost 54c. How much should a full box cost? _____

9.  Alan has climbed 785m of a 1000 metre mountain. What decimal fraction of the mountain has he still to climb? _____

10. What must be added to 0·984 to make 1 unit? _____

11.  Ann spent 0·7 of her money and had €24 left. How much money had she at first? _____

12.  0·675 of the spectators at a match were adults. What decimal fraction of the spectators was children? _____

Written Problems

1. Find the sum of 8·965, 4·387 and 3·564. _____

2. (28·236) (19·458) Andy thought of the number 28·236. Avril thought of the number 19·458. What is the difference between the two numbers? _____

3. What must be added to the sum of 23·847 and 19·631 to make 52·346? _____

4. Write in decimal form and then find the sum of
$3\frac{297}{1000}$, $1\frac{23}{100}$ and $2\frac{59}{1000}$. _____

5. By how much is $9\frac{63}{1000}$ greater than the sum of $3\frac{417}{1000}$ and $2\frac{9}{1000}$? _____
(Use decimals.)

6. There are 760 people living in a town. 0·4 of them are adults. How many children live in the town? _____

7. Joe spent 0·8 of his money and had €60 left. How much money had he at first? _____

8. A farmer sold 0·3 of his animals and had 189 animals left. How many animals had he at first? _____

9. Jim climbed 485m of a 1000 metre mountain.
After a rest, he climbed another 267m.
What decimal fraction of the mountain had he then climbed? _____

10. By how much is the 8 in 58·267 greater than the 8 in 37·498? _____

11. 0·317 of the spectators at a football match were children. What decimal fraction of the spectators was adults? _____

12. There were 1000 lollipops in a box.
The shopkeeper sold 139 lollipops on Saturday and 267 on Sunday.
What decimal fraction of the lollipops was still left? _____

1000 lollies

12. Lines and Angles

1. What kind of angle is each of these?
(Choose from **right**, **acute**, **straight**, **reflex** or **obtuse**.)

(a)

_____

(b)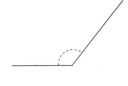

_____

(c)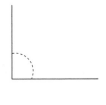

_____

(d)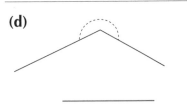

_____

(e)

_____

(f)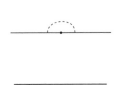

_____

2. The hands of a clock make **two** kinds of **angles**
(**except** when the hands overlap).
Name the **two angles** made by the hands of each of these clocks.

(a)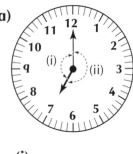

(i) _____

(ii) _____

(b)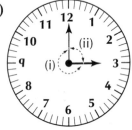

(i) _____

(ii) _____

(c)

(i) _____

(ii) _____

3. Complete these.

(a) When it is 6 o'clock, the two angles made by the hands are _____ angles.

(b) When it is 9 o'clock, one angle is _____ and the other angle is _____.

(c) When it is 4 o'clock, one angle is _____ and the other angle is _____.

(d) When it is 1 o'clock, one angle is _____ and the other angle is _____.

38

4. Angles are measured in degrees.
There are **360°** in a **full turn**.
We use a **protractor** to measure angles.
How many degrees are there in

(a) half of a full turn? _____

(b) a quarter of a full turn? _____

5. Use your **protractor** to find the number of degrees in each of these angles.
(**Estimate** first.)

(a)

Estimate _____
Measure _____

(b)

Estimate _____
Measure _____

(c)

Estimate _____
Measure _____

(d)

Estimate _____
Measure _____

(e)

Estimate _____
Measure _____

(f)

Estimate _____
Measure _____

6. Using a **pencil** and **protractor**, draw angles the following sizes.

(a)   40°

(b)   80°

_____

_____

(c)   100°

(d)   140°

_____

_____

7. Measure and write the angles inside each of these triangles. Find the sum of the angles in each.

(a)

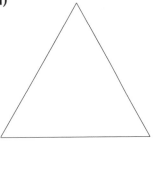

_____

(b)

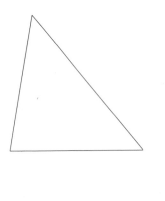

_____

(c)

_____

(d) The three angles of a triangle add up to _____ degrees.

(e) The three angles of a triangle always add up to _____ right angles.

40

8. Calculate the number of degrees in the **unmeasured** angle in each of these triangles.

(a)

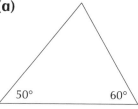

50°   60°

(b)

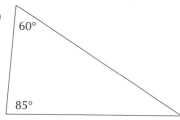

60°

85°

(c)

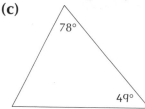

78°

49°

9. Calculate the number of degrees in each **obtuse** angle.

(a)

55°

(b)

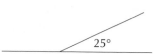

25°

(c)

74°

10. Here is a drawing of a compass.

A compass is used for navigation at sea, for orienteering or for other pursuits.

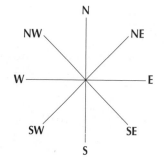

(a) Through how many degrees must I turn to go from facing **N** to facing **S**? _____

(b) Through how many degrees must I turn (clockwise) to go from facing **W** to facing **NE**? _____

(c) A ship was facing **NW**. It turned 90° anticlockwise. What direction was it then facing? _____

(d) A ship was sailing **SE**. It turned 135° clockwise. What direction was it then facing? _____

(e) What is the smallest number of degrees through which a ship must turn to go from facing **NW** to **E**? _____

41

13. Number Theory

$$3 \times 1 = 3 \quad \Rightarrow \quad$$ 3 is a **prime** number.
(It has only two divisors.)

$$4 \times 1 = 4$$
and $2 \times 2 = 4$ $\quad \Rightarrow \quad$ 4 is a **composite** number.
(It has more than **two** divisors.)

Remember

(a) The only factors/divisors a **prime** number has are itself and one.

(b) A **composite** number has other factors/divisors besides itself and one.

(c) The number 1 is neither a prime number nor a composite number.

1. Write the **prime** numbers contained in the following list.
   2, 5, 8, 13, 15, 20, 21 and 29 _____

2. Write the **composite** numbers contained in the following list.
   6, 7, 9, 11, 17, 18, 23 and 27 _____

3. Make a list of all the **prime** numbers less than 20.
   _____

4. Make a list of all the **composite** numbers less than 15.
   _____

We can find all the prime numbers up to 100 using a method known as
The Sieve of Eratosthenes (it lets all the **composite** numbers through the sieve and keeps the **primes**).

1	2	3	4	5	6	7	8	9	10
11	12	13	14	15	16	17	18	19	20
21	22	23	24	25	26	27	28	29	30
31	32	33	34	35	36	37	38	39	40
41	42	43	44	45	46	47	48	49	50
51	52	53	54	55	56	57	58	59	60
61	62	63	64	65	66	67	68	69	70
71	72	73	74	75	76	77	78	79	80
81	82	83	84	85	86	87	88	89	90
91	92	93	94	95	96	97	98	99	100

(i) Cross out square 1.

(ii) Leave square 2 white but colour all the multiples of 2 up to 100 (all the even numbers).

(iii) Leave square 3 white but colour all the multiples of 3 not already coloured.

(iv) Leave square 5 white but colour all the multiples of 5 not already coloured.

(v) Leave square 7 white but colour all the multiples of 7 not already coloured.

The **numbers** not coloured are the **prime numbers**.

5. Write the prime numbers contained in the following list.
   31, 33, 37, 39, 41 and 43 _____

6. Write the composite numbers contained in the following list.
   60, 61, 63, 65, 67 and 69 _____

7. Write **true** or **false** for each of these statements.
   (a) All odd numbers greater than 1 are prime numbers. _____
   (b) All even numbers greater than 1 are composite numbers. _____

8. Supply the **missing word** to make each statement true.
   (a) When I add two even numbers I always get an _____ number.
   (b) When I add two odd numbers I always get an _____ number.
   (c) When I add an odd and an even number I always get an _____ number.
   (d) When I multiply two even numbers I always get an _____ number.
   (e) When I multiply two odd numbers I always get an _____ number.
   (f) When I multiply an odd number by an even number
   I always get an _____ number.

9. Write the square numbers contained in the following list.
   1, 3, 5, 9, 12, 16 and 25 _____

10. Write all the square numbers from 30 up to 100. _____

11. What square number do I get when I add
    the first four odd numbers (1 + 3 + 5 + 7)? _____

12. What square number do I get when I add these odd numbers?
    (**You may use your calculator to help you.**)
    (a) The first six odd numbers. _____
    (b) The first seven odd numbers. _____
    (c) The first eight odd numbers. _____
    (d) The first nine odd numbers. _____
    (e) The first ten odd numbers. _____

13. Another name for composite numbers is **rectangular** numbers.
    Write the rectangular numbers contained in this list.
    50, 51, 53, 55, 57 and 59. _____

14. If a number has factors besides itself and 1, it is a rectangular number.
    Write the rectangular numbers contained in this list.
    29, 39, 49, 73, 75, 79 and 81 _____

14. Percentages

Mental Computation (A)

1. What **(i) fraction** and **(ii) percentage** of each shape is shaded?

   (a) 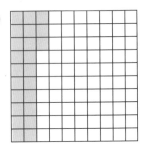   **(b)** 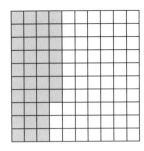   **(c)**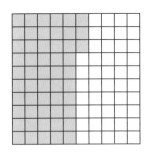

   (i) _____   (ii) _____   (i) _____   (ii) _____   (i) _____   (ii) _____

2. **(a)** Colour 17% of this shape.   **(b)** Colour 45% of this shape.   **(c)** Colour 74% of this shape.

   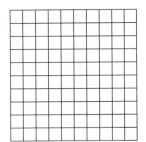   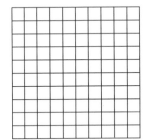   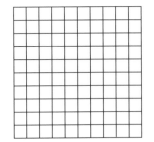

3. $\frac{1}{10} = \frac{}{100} =$ _____%

4. $\frac{2}{10} = \frac{}{100} =$ _____%

5. $\frac{3}{10} = \frac{}{100} =$ _____%

6. $\frac{5}{10} = \frac{}{100} =$ _____%

7. $\frac{7}{10} = \frac{}{100} =$ _____%

8. $\frac{8}{10} = \frac{}{100} =$ _____%

9. $\frac{9}{10} = \frac{}{100} =$ _____%

10. $\frac{10}{10} = \frac{}{100} =$ _____%

Add these **fractions** and then write as **percentages**.

11. $\frac{1}{10} + \frac{9}{100} = \frac{}{100} =$ _____%

12. $\frac{3}{10} + \frac{7}{100} = \frac{}{100} =$ _____%

13. $\frac{5}{10} + \frac{8}{100} = \frac{}{100} =$ _____%

14. $\frac{7}{10} + \frac{9}{100} = \frac{}{100} =$ _____%

Mental Computation (B)

Write these percentages as **tenths** and **hundredths**.

1. $13\% = \dfrac{}{10} + \dfrac{}{100}$

2. $17\% = \dfrac{}{10} + \dfrac{}{100}$

3. $29\% = \dfrac{}{10} + \dfrac{}{100}$

4. $41\% = \dfrac{}{10} + \dfrac{}{100}$

5. $73\% = \dfrac{}{10} + \dfrac{}{100}$

6. $97\% = \dfrac{}{10} + \dfrac{}{100}$

7. Write the missing **percentages** on this **number line**.

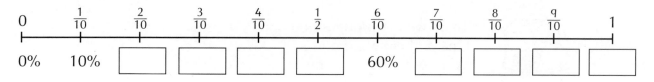

Write these fractions as **hundredths** and then as **percentages**.

8. $\dfrac{1}{5} = \dfrac{}{100} = $ _____%

9. $\dfrac{2}{5} = \dfrac{}{100} = $ _____%

10. $\dfrac{3}{5} = \dfrac{}{100} = $ _____%

11. $\dfrac{4}{5} = \dfrac{}{100} = $ _____%

12. $\dfrac{1}{2} = \dfrac{}{100} = $ _____%

13. $\dfrac{1}{4} = \dfrac{}{100} = $ _____%

14. $\dfrac{3}{4} = \dfrac{}{100} = $ _____%

15. $\dfrac{1}{20} = \dfrac{}{100} = $ _____%

16. $\dfrac{3}{20} = \dfrac{}{100} = $ _____%

17. $\dfrac{7}{20} = \dfrac{}{100} = $ _____%

Write the missing **percentage** in each of these.

18. $25\% + 25\% + $ _____$\% = 1$

19. $30\% + 50\% + $ _____$\% = 1$

20. $35\% + 35\% + $ _____$\% = 1$

21. $40\% + 35\% + $ _____$\% = 1$

22. $60\% + 25\% + $ _____$\% = 1$

23. $45\% + 25\% + $ _____$\% = 1$

24. $35\% + 55\% + $ _____$\% = 1$

25. $50\% + 45\% + $ _____$\% = 1$

Written Problems (A)

1. A farmer had 100 sheep. He sold 37 of them.
   What percentage of them did he sell? _____

2. There are 100 children in a club. 60 of them are girls.
   What percentage of them are boys? _____

3. Ten cars were parked outside the school. 3 of them were black.
   What percentage of the cars was black? _____

4. Ten of the 20 apples in a bag are green.
   What percentage of the apples is green? _____

5. There were 4 oranges in a bag.
   One of them was bad.
   What percentage of the oranges was bad? _____

6. 3 of the 4 children in a family are girls.
   What percentage of the family is girls? _____

7. A farmer had 60 cattle.
   He sold 30% of them.
   How many cattle did he sell? _____

8. John had 70 stamps.
   He gave 10% of them to Joan.
   How many stamps had he left? _____

9. Jim had €50. He spent 70% of it buying a helmet.
   How much did he pay for the helmet? _____

10. 40% of the apples in a box were red.
    If there were 32 red apples,
    how many apples were in the box altogether? _____

11. Mark had 32 marbles.
    He lost 8 of them.
    What percentage of them did he lose? _____

12. Alan had €150.
    He spent 50% of it buying a coat.
    What was the cost of the coat? _____

Mental Problems (B)

1. Enda spent 85% of his money buying a bicycle.
   What percentage of his money had he left? _____

2. Pat had €48. He spent 25% of it buying a football.
   What was the cost of the football? _____

3. There were 20 oranges in a box. 3 of them were bad.
   What percentage of them was bad? _____

4. 7 of the 20 children in a group are boys.
   What percentage of them is boys? _____

5. Linda had €36.
   She spent 75% of it buying a hat.
   What was the price of the hat? _____

6. There were 5 apples in a bag.
   2 of them were red.
   What percentage of the apples was red? _____

7. There were 45 lollipops in a jar.
   The shopkeeper sold 40% of them.
   How many lollipops did she sell? _____

8. A farmer had 400 sheep. She sold 9% of them.
   How many sheep did she sell? _____

9. 30% of the children in a school have brown hair.
   If 36 children have brown hair,
   how many children are there in the school? _____

10. There are 5 children in a family.
    3 of them are girls.
    What percentage of the family is girls? _____

11. There are 35 children in a club.
    80% of them like football.
    How many of them like football? _____

12. Kevin spent 50% of his money in one shop and 30% in another.
    He then had €11 left.
    How much money had he at first? _____

15. Fractions, Decimals and Percentages

Mental Computation (A)

Write these decimals as **fractions** and as **percentages**.

1. $0.3 = \boxed{} = \underline{}\%$

2. $0.7 = \boxed{} = \underline{}\%$

3. $0.9 = \boxed{} = \underline{}\%$

4. $0.1 = \boxed{} = \underline{}\%$

5. $0.13 = \boxed{} = \underline{}\%$

6. $0.19 = \boxed{} = \underline{}\%$

7. $0.27 = \boxed{} = \underline{}\%$

8. $0.39 = \boxed{} = \underline{}\%$

9. $0.53 = \boxed{} = \underline{}\%$

10. $0.89 = \boxed{} = \underline{}\%$

Write each of these percentages as **decimals**.

11. $17\% = \underline{}$
12. $23\% = \underline{}$
13. $36\% = \underline{}$
14. $47\% = \underline{}$

15. $54\% = \underline{}$
16. $69\% = \underline{}$
17. $78\% = \underline{}$
18. $95\% = \underline{}$

Write each of these decimals as **percentages**.

19. $0.18 = \underline{}$
20. $0.24 = \underline{}$
21. $0.63 = \underline{}$
22. $0.75 = \underline{}$

23. $0.91 = \underline{}$
24. $0.9 = \underline{}$
25. $0.09 = \underline{}$
26. $0.03 = \underline{}$

What **(i) fraction**, **(ii) decimal fraction** and **(iii) percentage** of each of these shapes is shaded?

27.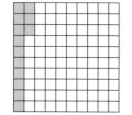

(i) _____

(ii) _____

(iii) _____

28.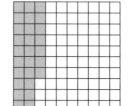

(i) _____

(ii) _____

(iii) _____

29.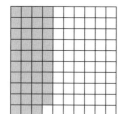

(i) _____

(ii) _____

(iii) _____

30.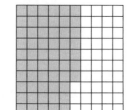

(i) _____

(ii) _____

(iii) _____

48

Mental Computation (B)

Write these fractions as **decimals** and as **percentages**.

1. $\frac{7}{100}$ = _____ = _____   2. $\frac{9}{100}$ = _____ = _____

3. $\frac{1}{2}$ = _____ = _____   4. $\frac{1}{4}$ = _____ = _____

5. $\frac{3}{4}$ = _____ = _____   6. $\frac{1}{5}$ = _____ = _____

7. $\frac{2}{5}$ = _____ = _____   8. $\frac{3}{5}$ = _____ = _____

9. $\frac{4}{5}$ = _____ = _____   10. $\frac{1}{20}$ = _____ = _____

11. $\frac{3}{20}$ = _____ = _____   12. $\frac{7}{20}$ = _____ = _____

13. $\frac{9}{20}$ = _____ = _____   14. $\frac{11}{20}$ = _____ = _____

15. $\frac{1}{50}$ = _____ = _____   16. $\frac{1}{25}$ = _____ = _____

17. Complete this table.

fraction	$\frac{11}{100}$	$\frac{27}{100}$				$\frac{1}{5}$	
decimal	0·11		0·43		0·8		0·5
percentage	11%			9%			

18. 10% of 70 = _____   19. 20% of 30 = _____   20. 50% of 24 = _____

21. 25% of 32 = _____   22. 75% of 12 = _____   23. 40% of 25 = _____

24. 5% of 40 = _____   25. 60% of 35 = _____

Write the **missing percentages** on these number lines.

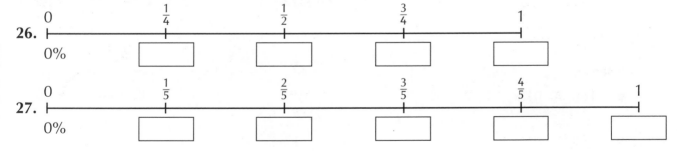

Arrange in order, starting with the **smallest**.

28. $\frac{1}{5}$, 19%, 0·21   29. 0·65, $\frac{3}{5}$, 68%   30. 78%, $\frac{3}{4}$, 0·8

_____ _____ _____   _____ _____ _____   _____ _____ _____

49

Written Computation (A)

1. $\frac{3}{4}$ of 188 = _____
2. $\frac{2}{5}$ of 185 = _____
3. $\frac{4}{5}$ of 365 = _____

4. 0·3 of 280 = _____
5. 0·7 of 360 = _____
6. 0·9 of 420 = _____

7. 30% of 170 = _____
8. 70% of 530 = _____
9. 90% of 680 = _____

10. 20% of 340 = _____
11. 40% of 490 = _____
12. 60% of 560 = _____

13. 50% of 154 = _____
14. 25% of 276 = _____
15. 75% of 352 = _____

16. 20% of 355 = _____
17. 40% of 195 = _____
18. 60% of 425 = _____

19. 80% of 475 = _____
20. 75% of 676 = _____
21. 50% of 592 = _____

22. 90% of 570 = _____
23. 60% of 825 = _____
24. 75% of 936 = _____

Written Computation (B)

Increase.
1. 470 by 10%
2. 760 by 10%
3. 930 by 10%

4. 250 by 20%
5. 360 by 20%
6. 480 by 20%

7. 172 by 25%
8. 256 by 25%
9. 372 by 25%

10. 238 by 50%
11. 260 by 30%
12. 340 by 70%

13. 135 by 40%
14. 245 by 60%
15. 315 by 80%

Decrease.
16. 160 by 10%
17. 280 by 10%
18. 340 by 10%

19. 135 by 20%
20. 276 by 25%
21. 178 by 50%

22. 280 by 30%
23. 295 by 40%
24. 415 by 60%

Mental Problems

1. Fred had €10. He bought a ball for €3.
   What percentage of his money had he left? _____

2. A farmer had 250 sheep.
   He sold 10% of them.
   How many sheep did he sell? _____

3. 50% of the children in a school are girls. If there are 70 girls,
   how many children attend the school altogether? _____

4. There are 55 apples in a box.
   0·2 of them are red.
   How many red apples are there? _____

5. $\frac{3}{4}$ of the trees in a wood are evergreen. If there are 60 evergreen trees,
   how many trees altogether are there in the wood? _____

6. Gary had €48.
   He spent 75% on football boots.
   How much did the football boots cost? _____

7. There were 25 chocolates in a box.
   The children ate 10 of them.
   What percentage of them did they eat? _____

8. Paul has 60 stamps.
   Pat has 10% more than that.
   How many stamps has Pat? _____

9. Last week there were 25 plums in each box.
   This week there are 20% extra in each box.
   How many plums are there in each box this week? _____

10. There were 32 people at swimming class two weeks ago.
    There were 25% less last week.
    How many people were at swimming class last week? _____

11. 60% of the children in a club are girls.
    If there are 36 girls,
    how many children are there in the club altogether? _____

    40 = boys

12. Joe spent 40% of his money in one shop and 35% in another.
    He then had €12 left.
    How much money had he at first? _____

51

Written Problems

1. 570 spectators attended a football match one Sunday.
   30% of that number attended the next Sunday.
   How many attended that Sunday? _____

2. 490 children attend a school.
   40% of them are boys.
   How many boys attend the school? _____

3. There are 296 beech trees in a forest.
   There are also 75% of that number ash trees.
   How many ash trees are there in the forest? _____

4. Paul has read 60% of the 185 pages in his book.
   How many pages has he read? _____

5. There are 135 apples in a box.
   0·8 of them are green.
   How many green apples are there in the box? _____

6. Gerard spent $\frac{5}{8}$ of his money buying a coat.
   If the coat cost €120, how much money had he at first? _____

7. A farmer has 230 sheep.
   A second farmer has 20% more sheep than that.
   How many sheep has the second farmer? _____

8. A bus set out on a journey of 245km.
   When 80% of the journey had been completed,
   how far had it still to go? _____

9. Increase 356 by 25%. _____

10. 970 people attended a concert this year.
    30% less than that attended last year.
    How many people attended last year? _____

11. Last year a TV set cost €465.
    This year it costs 20% more.
    How much does it cost this year? _____

12. A bicycle cost €272 last year.
    It costs 25% less this year.
    How much does it cost this year? _____

16. 3-D Shapes

1. Name each of these **3-D shapes**.
(Choose from **cube, cuboid, cone, cylinder, pyramid, triangular prism, sphere**.)

(a)

(b)

(c)

(d)

_____

_____

_____

_____

(e)

(f)

(g)

(h)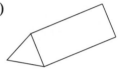

_____

_____

_____

_____

2. Which **shape** am I?

(a) I have 1 square face and 4 equal triangular faces. _____

(b) I have 6 square faces. _____

(c) I have 2 circular faces and 1 curved face. _____

(d) I have 6 rectangular faces. My opposite faces are equal. _____

(e) I have 1 circular face and 1 curved face. _____

(f) I have 2 triangular faces and 3 rectangular faces. _____

3. Supply the **missing numbers** to make these statements true.

(a) A cube has ____ faces, ____ edges and ____ vertices (corners).

(b) A cuboid has ____ faces, ____ edges and ____ vertices.

(c) A pyramid has ____ faces, ____ edges and ____ vertices.

(d) A sphere has ____ faces, ____ edges and ____ vertices.

(e) A triangular prism has ____ faces, ____ edges and ____ vertices.

(f) A cone has ____ faces, ____ edges and ____ vertices.

(g) A cylinder has ____ faces, ____ edges and ____ vertices.

4. Here are the **nets** of some **3-D shapes**. Can you identify them?

(a)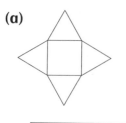

_____

(b)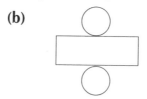

_____

(c)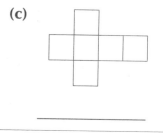

_____

(d)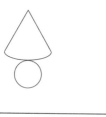

_____

(e)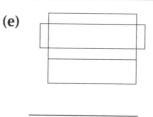

_____

(f)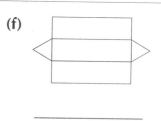

_____

5. A **tetrahedron** is a **triangular-based pyramid**.
(The word **tetra** means **four** in the Greek language.)

Here is the net of a tetrahedron.
It has 4 faces and each face is an equilateral triangle.

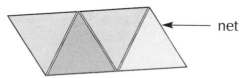 ← net

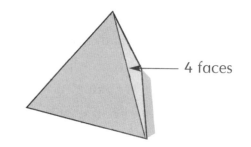 — 4 faces

(a) A tetrahedron has _____ edges.

(b) A tetrahedron has _____ vertices.

6. Here is a drawing of a **pentagonal prism**.

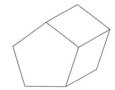

(a) It has _____ faces.

(b) 5 of its faces are _____ and 2 are _____.

(c) It has _____ edges and _____ vertices.

7. This is a drawing of a **hexagonal prism**.

(a) It has _____ faces.

(b) 6 of its faces are _____ and 2 are _____.

(c) It has _____ edges and _____ vertices.

17. Time

Mental Computation

Write as **hours** and **minutes**.

1. 80 mins _____
2. 105 mins _____
3. 130 mins _____
4. 150 mins _____

5. 94 mins _____
6. 108 mins _____
7. 117 mins _____
8. 138 mins _____

Write as **minutes**.

9. 1 hr 25 mins _____
10. 1 hr 50 mins _____
11. 2 hrs 5 mins _____
12. 2 hrs 55 mins _____

13. 1 hr 37 mins _____
14. 1 hr 53 mins _____
15. 2 hrs 16 mins _____
16. 2 hrs 48 mins _____

Write these times in **digital form** using **am** or **pm**.

17. $\frac{1}{2}$ past 3 in the morning. _____
18. $\frac{1}{4}$ past 8 in the evening. _____
19. 20 to 4 in the afternoon. _____
20. 25 to 12 at night. _____
21. $\frac{1}{4}$ to 10 in the morning. _____
22. 10 to 7 in the evening. _____

Write these times using the **24-hour clock** system (always use **four** digits).

23. 6.30 am _____
24. 9.30 am _____
25. 2.15 pm _____
26. 3.45 pm _____

27. 7.28 pm _____
28. 10.47 am _____
29. 9.53 pm _____
30. 11.16 pm _____

Write the following **24-hour** times as **am** or **pm** times

31. 05:20 _____
32. 17:35 _____
33. 20:50 _____
34. 22:28 _____

How many **hours** and **minutes** are there from

35. 03:15 to 05:30? _____
36. 10:30 to 13:00? _____
37. 14:25 to 16:40? _____
38. 18:50 to 21:10? _____
39. 19:45 to 22:15? _____
40. 21:20 to 23:55? _____

55

Written Computation (A)

	hrs	mins			hrs	mins			hrs	mins			hrs	mins
1.	1	45	**2.**		1	27	**3.**		2	38	**4.**		2	19
	2	25			2	38			3	47			4	36
	+ 1	35			+ 1	46			+ 1	29			+ 1	28

	hrs	mins			hrs	mins			hrs	mins			hrs	mins
5.	4	15	**6.**		5	26	**7.**		6	17	**8.**		7	51
	− 1	50			− 2	38			− 3	49			− 2	58

	hrs	mins			hrs	mins			hrs	mins			hrs	mins
9.	1	35	**10.**		1	28	**11.**		1	17	**12.**		2	24
	× 3				× 4				× 5				× 6	

Written Computation (B)

	hrs	mins			hrs	mins			hrs	mins			hrs	mins
1.	2	37	**2.**		3	26	**3.**		2	39	**4.**		3	56
	1	49			2	47			4	48			2	29
	+ 3	28			+ 2	58			+ 1	54			+ 1	37

	hrs	mins			hrs	mins			hrs	mins			hrs	mins
5.	5	23	**6.**		6	14	**7.**		7	32	**8.**		9	26
	− 2	37			− 1	39			− 3	53			− 4	47

	hrs	mins			hrs	mins			hrs	mins			hrs	mins
9.	2	28	**10.**		2	36	**11.**		2	27	**12.**		1	18
	× 4				× 3				× 5				× 6	

Mental Problems

1. A bus took $1\frac{1}{4}$ hours to complete a journey.
   How many minutes did the journey take? _____

2. A sports programme started on TV at 14:30.
   If the programme lasted 70 minutes, at what time did it end? _____

3. School starts at 09:20.
   Emma arrived 35 minutes before starting time.
   At what time did she arrive? _____

4. A football match was due to start at 14:40.
   If it was 35 minutes late starting, at what time did it start? _____

5. A motorcyclist completed a journey in 45 minutes.
   If the starting time was 11:25,
   at what time did the journey finish? _____

6. One evening, Evin spent $1\frac{3}{4}$ hours doing his homework.
   How many minutes was what? _____   *misprint

7. A film started at 18:20.
   If the film lasted $2\frac{1}{2}$ hours, at what time did it end? _____

8. A concert started at 15:25 and finished at 18:40.
   How many hours and minutes did the concert last? ____hrs ____mins

9. Each half of a football match lasts 45 minutes.
   If there is a 15-minute break at half-time, how many hours and
   minutes from the start of the match to the end? ____hrs ____mins

10. Pam's flight is due to leave at 16:10.
    If she checks in $1\frac{1}{2}$ hours before departure time,
    at what time does she check in? _____

11. A train left the station at 16:50.
    If the journey lasted $2\frac{1}{4}$ hours, at what time did it end? _____

12. A group of children went on a hike at 08:45.
    They arrived back at 12:10.
    How many hours and minutes did the hike last? ____hrs ____mins

57

Written Problems

1. Joe left home at $\frac{1}{4}$ past 5 one afternoon.
He returned home at 7.40 pm.
For how many hours and minutes was he away? ____hrs ____mins

2. Barbara went shopping at $\frac{1}{4}$ to 11 one Saturday.
She got home at 17:30.
How long was she away from home? ____hrs ____mins

3. Ivan arrived at the airport at 25 minutes to 2 one afternoon.
His flight left at 15:12.
How long did he spend at the airport? ____hrs ____mins

4. A film started at 16:23.
If the film lasted 1 hr 56 minutes, at what time did it end? _____

5. The first bus from Galway to Dublin leaves at 6.35 am.
If the journey takes 2 hrs 57 mins,
at what time is it due in Dublin? _____

6. A fireworks display started at 25 minutes past 9 one evening.
It finished at 23:07.
How long did the display last? ____hrs ____mins

7. Peter watched sport on TV from 11.20 am to 1.08 pm.
He also watched a nature programme for 57 minutes.
How long altogether did he spend watching TV? ____hrs ____mins

8. How many hours and minutes are there from 9.38 am to 2.25 pm? ____hrs ____mins

9. A train left the station at 17:26.
If the journey took 2 hrs 47 mins, at what time did it arrive? _____

10. How many hours and minutes are there from 20 minutes to 8 in the morning
to 17 minutes past 3 in the afternoon? ____hrs ____mins

11. Dad arrived home from work one evening at 7.12 pm.
He had left home at 8.27 am that morning.
How long was he away from home? ____hrs ____mins

12. Ann watched a science programme on TV from 11:36 to 12:14.
She also watched a sports programme on TV from 14:47 to 16:06.
How long altogether did she spend watching TV? ____hrs ____mins

18. Area and Perimeter

Mental Computation (A)

What is the **area** of each shape in **square centimetres** (cm^2)?

1. 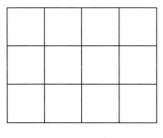 _____

2. 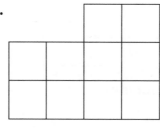 _____

3. 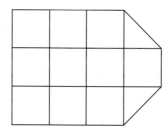 _____

4. 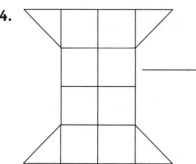 _____

5. 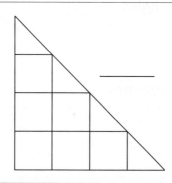 _____

6. 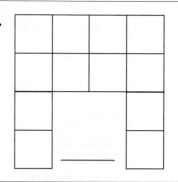 _____

What is the **area** of each of these **rectangles**?

7. 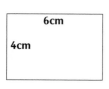 _____

8. 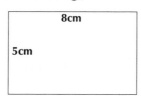 _____

9. 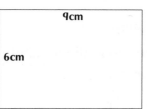 _____

Find the **area** of the following **rectangles**.

10. Length 7cm, width 6cm _____   **11.** Length 8cm, width 4cm _____

12. Length 9cm, width 7cm _____   **13.** Length 10cm, width 9cm _____

Find the **perimeter** of the following **rectangles**.

14. Length 9cm, width 8cm _____   **15.** Length 10cm, width 6cm _____

16. Length 12cm, width 8cm _____   **17.** Length 14cm, width 7cm _____

Mental Computation (B)

What is the **area** of each shape in **square metres** (m^2)?

1.

8m
3m

2.

10m
4m

3.

9m
5m

_____   _____   _____

Find the **area** of the following **rectangles**.

    4. Length 7m, width 5m _____   **5.** Length 9m, width 6m _____

    6. Length 10m, width 7m _____   **7.** Length 9m, width 8m _____

Find the **perimeter** of these **rectangles**.

    8. Length 11m, width 4m _____   **9.** Length 12m, width 6m _____

  10. Length 25m, width 10m _____   **11.** Length 20m, width 15m _____

12. Complete this table of rectangles.

Rectangle	(a)	(b)	(c)	(d)	(e)
length	7m	6m			9m
width	3m		5m	6m	
perimeter			24m		32m
area		30m²		48m²	

Written Computation

Find the **area** and the **perimeter** of each shape.

1.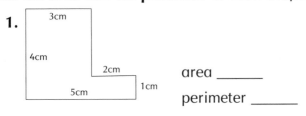

    area _____

    perimeter _____

2.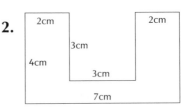

    area _____

    perimeter _____

3.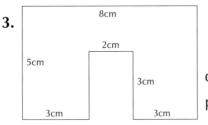

    area _____

    perimeter _____

4.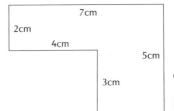

    area _____

    perimeter _____

Mental Problems

1. A birthday card is 20cm long and 10cm wide. What is its area? _____

2. A garden shed is 6m long and 4m wide. What is the area of the shed floor? _____

3. A book is 25cm long and 20cm wide. What is its perimeter? _____

4. What is the perimeter of a hall 40m long and 20m wide? _____

5. 12cm

A rectangle 12cm long has a perimeter of 36cm. What is its width? _____

6. 9cm

A rectangle 9cm long has an area of 63cm^2. What is its width? _____

7. 8cm

What is the area of a square if each side is 8cm in length? _____

8. What is the perimeter of a square if its area is 49cm^2? _____

9. What is the area of a square if its perimeter is 36cm? _____

10. 8m

The length of a rectangle is double its width. If its width is 8m, what is its perimeter? _____

11. 11m

The perimeter of a rectangle is 36m. If its length is 11m, what is its area? _____

12. 6m 5m

What is the cost of carpeting a room 6m long and 5m wide at €20 per square metre? _____

61

Written Problems

1. **24cm** / **25cm** — A sheet of paper is 25cm long and 24cm wide. What is its area? _____

2. A rectangular garden is 36m long and 23m wide. What is the area of the garden? _____

3. What is the perimeter of a rectangular playground 45m long and 28m wide? _____

4. **32cm** — A rectangle 32m long has a perimeter of 98cm. What is its width? _____

5. **26cm** — A rectangle 26cm long has an area of 312cm^2. What is its perimeter? _____

6. What is the area of a square if its perimeter is 72cm? _____

7. **28m** — The perimeter of a rectangular lawn is 88m. If its length is 28m, what is its area? _____

8. **17m** — The length of a rectangular lawn is double its width. If its width is 17m, what is its area? _____

9. **8m** / **4m** — What is the cost of carpeting a room 8m long and 4m wide at €27 per square metre? _____

10. A rectangle 32m long has the same perimeter as a square of side 24m. What is the area of the rectangle? _____

11. What will it cost to fence in a garden 17m long and 13m wide if fencing costs €16 per metre? _____

12. This drawing is the plan of a room. How much will it cost to put a timber floor in the room at €28 per square metre? _____

6m / **2m** / **5m** / **3m**

62

19. The Circle

1. Write the names for the different parts of a circle.
(Choose from **radius, diameter, centre, circumference**.)

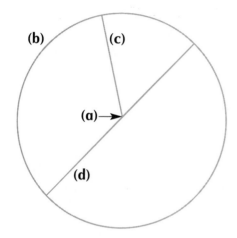

(a) The point at the middle of the circle is called the _____.

(b) The curved outer edge of the circle is called the _____.

(c) A line joining the centre to the circumference is called the _____.

(d) A line joining one point of the circumference with another and going through the centre is called a _____.

2. Using a **hula-hoop** (or a **tyre** of a bicycle) find these measurements.

(a) The diameter of the hula-hoop. _____

(b) The radius of the hula-hoop. _____

(c) Using a string, find the length of the circumference. _____

(d) The circumference is about _____ times the diameter.

3. Having discovered that the **circumference** of a **circle** is about **three times** the **diameter**, calculate the answers to the following questions.

(a) What is the approximate length of the circumference of a wheel with a diameter of 32cm? _____

(b) What is the approximate length of the diameter of a circle if its circumference is 78cm? _____

(c) The radius of a circle is 14cm.
What is the approximate length of its circumference? _____

4. Complete these tables about circles (**approximate circumference**).

(a)	radius __8cm__	diameter _____	circumference _____
(b)	radius _____	diameter __18cm__	circumference _____

5. Find the **approximate area** of each of these **circles** in **square centimetres** (cm^2).

Remember (i) Count all the whole squares first.

(ii) Count half of a square or more as a full square.

(iii) Ignore amounts less than half a square.

(a)

(b)

(c)

(a) _____

(b) _____

(c)_____

6. Using a **compass** and a **ruler**, draw the following circles:
(a) having a radius of 3cm, (b) having a radius of $3\frac{1}{2}$ cm.

(a)

(b)

7. What is the **approximate area** of the **circles** you have drawn? (a) _____ (b) _____

8. Using your **compass**, make designs based on the **circle** on a sheet of paper.
Colour the designs.

20. Money

Mental Computation

1. €10 − €7·40 = _____
2. €10 − €4·25 = _____
3. €10 − €3·68 = _____
4. €20 − €6·50 = _____
5. €20 − €8·15 = _____
6. €20 − €4·37 = _____
7. $\frac{2}{3}$ of €24 = _____
8. $\frac{2}{5}$ of €20 = _____
9. $\frac{3}{4}$ of €28 = _____
10. $\frac{5}{6}$ of €42 = _____
11. $\frac{3}{8}$ of €40 = _____
12. $\frac{5}{9}$ of €54 = _____
13. 0·3 of €60 = _____
14. 0·7 of €80 = _____
15. 0·4 of €30 = _____
16. 10% of €80 = _____
17. 30% of €90 = _____
18. 25% of €36 = _____
19. 75% of €32 = _____
20. 50% of €86 = _____
21. 20% of €35 = _____
22. 40% of €45 = _____
23. 5% of €40 = _____
24. 60% of €25 = _____

Increase.

25. €30 by 10% = _____
26. €50 by 20% = _____
27. €24 by 25% = _____

Decrease.

28. €40 by 10% = _____
29. €20 by 25% = _____
30. €18 by 50% = _____

Written Computation

1.
```
  €36·89
  €23·28
+ €17·64
_____
```

2.
```
  €24·57
  €37·69
+ €19·75
_____
```

3.
```
  €18·76
  €28·57
+ €26·98
_____
```

4.
```
  €39·56
  €27·09
+ €14·76
_____
```

5.
```
  €54·36
− €19·57
_____
```

6.
```
  €72·14
− €35·65
_____
```

7.
```
  €60·34
− €23·58
_____
```

8.
```
  €90·00
− €37·81
_____
```

9.
```
  €16·38
×      3
_____
```

10.
```
  €13·78
×      7
_____
```

11.
```
  €15·97
×      6
_____
```

12.
```
  €19·69
×      4
_____
```

13. 4)€9·56
14. 5)€8·95
15. 6)€8·28
16. 7)€9·66

65

17. 5)€6·85

_____ × 3

_____

18. 8)€9·76

_____ × 7

_____

19. 6)€8·58

_____ × 5

_____

20. 9)€9·54

_____ × 4

_____

Mental Problems

1. Clare had €10. She bought a scarf for €7·45. How much money had she left? _____

2. Ann has €20. Andrew has €13·67. How much more money has Ann than Andrew? _____

3. Six oranges cost €2·14. How much should twelve oranges cost? _____

4. An apple costs 34c. How much should 20 apples cost? _____

5. Sue has €44. Sam has 0·75 of that amount. How much money has Sam? _____

6. Having spent $\frac{1}{4}$ of his money, Barry had €36 left. How much had he at first? _____

7. Rita spent 60% of her money buying a dress. If she had €48 left, how much money had she at first? _____

8. I spent $\frac{3}{4}$ of my money in one shop and 0·15 of it in another. What percentage of my money had I left? _____

9. A pair of football boots cost €45. Peter has saved 80% of the cost of the boots. How much money has he saved? _____

10. A fridge that cost €530 last year now costs 10% more. How much does it now cost? _____

11. During a sale, a television set was reduced by 20%. If the normal price was €400, what was the sale price? _____

12. Pat spent 80% of his money on a bicycle and had €40 left. What was the cost of the bicycle? _____

Written Problems

1. Jack bought football boots for €38·95 and a hurley for €23·40. What change had he from €70? _____

2. A jacket costs €65. Fiona had €28·65. Her mother gave her €16·85. How much more does she need to buy the jacket? _____

3. A scarf costs €7·85. What change had Tom from €40 when he bought 3 scarves? _____

4. Enda had €2·48 change from €5 when he bought 7 copybooks. What was the cost of one copybook? _____

5. Eight packets of peanuts cost €9·36. How much should five packets of peanuts cost? _____

6. A worker for a building company gets €24 per hour. What were his total earnings for a week if he worked 39 hours? _____

7. A car travels 15km on 1 litre of petrol. What is the cost of the petrol used on a journey of 135km at €0·98 per litre? _____

8. Alan spent 0·7 of his money buying clothes. If he had €19·65 left, how much had he at first? _____

9. Susan spent 60% of her money buying boots. If she had €56 left, how much had she at first? _____

10. A cooker that cost €670 last year now costs 10% more. How much does it now cost? _____

11. During a sale, the price a digital camera was reduced by 25%. If the normal price was €272, what was the sale price? _____

12. Joe spent 40% of his money in one shop and 35% in another. If he had €18·76 left, how much had he at first? _____

21. Length

Mental Computation

Write as **millimetres** (**mm**).

1. 2·6cm

2. 4·8cm

3. 7·9cm

4. 12·3cm

5. 3cm 4mm

6. 5cm 7mm

7. 9cm 8mm

8. 13cm 6mm

Write as **centimetres** using the **decimal point**.

9. 28mm

10. 67mm

11. 125mm

12. 142mm

13. 8cm 3mm

14. 9cm 7mm

15. 11cm 4mm

16. 16cm 8mm

Write as **metres** using the **decimal point**.

17. 165cm

18. 238cm

19. 308cm

20. 934cm

21. 4m 26cm

22. 6m 92cm

23. 8m 9cm

24. 12m 7cm

Write as **kilometres** (**km**) using the **decimal point**.

25. 2365m

26. 4609m

27. 5078m

28. 7006m

29. 1km 438m

30. 2km 360m

31. 4km 68m

32. 6km 9m

Write as **metres**.

33. 2km 190m

34. 4km 765m

35. 3km 78m

36. 5km 7m

37. $4\frac{1}{2}$km

38. $3\frac{7}{10}$km

39. $4\frac{1}{4}$km

40. $6\frac{3}{4}$km

41. 3·47km

42. 5·8km

43. 4·053km

44. 6·09km

68

Written Computation

1.
```
cm  mm
13   7
+ 4    9
_____
```

2.
```
cm  mm
26   3
- 12   8
_____
```

3.
```
 m  cm
14  69
+ 13  87
_____
```

4.
```
 m  cm
39  34
- 15  67
_____
```

5.
```
 m  cm
 1  38
   × 5
_____
```

6.
```
  38·7cm
+ 19·6cm
_____
```

7.
```
  29·4cm
- 13·5cm
_____
```

8.
```
  26·78m
+ 15·64m
_____
```

9.
```
  68·53m
- 43·79m
_____
```

10.
```
  2·37m
    × 4
_____
```

11.
```
  2·385km
  1·637km
+ 3·526km
_____
```

12.
```
  3·247km
  2·568km
+ 2·493km
_____
```

13.
```
  4·296km
  2·573km
+ 1·928km
_____
```

14.
```
  3·238km
  1·357km
+ 4·896km
_____
```

15.
```
  2·643km
  3·589km
+ 2·476km
_____
```

16.
```
  9·435km
- 2·673km
_____
```

17.
```
  8·326km
- 5·498km
_____
```

18.
```
  7·634km
- 3·978km
_____
```

19.
```
  9·046km
- 2·589km
_____
```

20.
```
  8·005km
- 3·237km
_____
```

21. 3 ⟌ 5·274km

22. 5 ⟌ 9·385km

23. 4 ⟌ 7·296km

24. 2 ⟌ 9·738km

25. 6 ⟌ 8·574km

26.
```
  2·367km
      × 3
_____
```

27.
```
  1·639km
      × 6
_____
```

28.
```
  3·492km
      × 2
_____
```

29.
```
  1·948km
      × 5
_____
```

30.
```
  2·379km
      × 4
_____
```

Before doing these, write each in **decimal form**.

31. $8cm \ 6mm + 7\frac{1}{2}cm + 9·8cm = $ _____

32. $4m \ 38cm + 9·65m + 6\frac{1}{4}m = $ _____

33. $3·672km + 2967m + 5\frac{7}{10}km = $ _____

34. $5km \ 384m + 3\frac{1}{4}km + 4·348km = $ _____

35. $(9cm \ 3mm + 4·9cm) - 86mm = $ _____

36. $(4m\ 76cm + 8·76m) - 9\frac{1}{2}m =$ _____

37. $(8·437km + 6\frac{3}{10}km) - 9276m =$ _____

38. $(5km\ 346m + 9\frac{1}{4}km) - 9·8km =$ _____

39. $(2·67m + 5\frac{3}{4}m) \times 3 =$ _____

40. $(2356m + 3·4km) \times 4 =$ _____

Mental Problems

1. A nail is 45mm long. Another nail is 5cm long.
Write the total length of the two nails in centimetres. _____

2. A pencil is 170mm long.
How many centimetres long is the pencil? _____

3. Joan is 148cm tall.
Express her height in metres using the decimal point. _____

4. Paul's step is 80cm.
How many metres does he walk if he takes 10 steps? _____

5. John walked 5285 metres.
Write the distance in kilometres using the decimal point. _____

6. When an athlete had completed 2650 metres of a 3km race,
how far had he still to go? _____

7. A metre of rope costs €1·20.
How much should 2m 50cm of rope cost? _____

8. A running track is 400m all around.
How many km did Jack run if he completed 7 laps? _____

9. Jim is 1m 35cm tall. Joe is 7cm taller.
Express Joe's height in metres using the decimal point. _____

10.  Susan can run 400m in 2 minutes.
How many km should she run in 8 minutes at the same speed? _____

11. From a ribbon 2m long, two pieces 45cm and 40cm were cut.
What length of ribbon was left? _____

12. 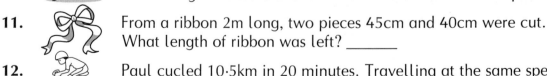 Paul cycled 10·5km in 20 minutes. Travelling at the same speed,
how far should he cycle in one hour? _____

Written Problems

1. Three pencils measure 18·5cm, $16\frac{3}{10}$cm and 155mm.
   What is the total length in cm of the pencils? _____

2. What is the total length of three planks of wood that measure 5·3 metres, 6m 45cm and $4\frac{7}{10}$m? _____

3. A chimney is 15m 62cm tall. Another chimney is 2·35m smaller.
   What is the height of the smaller chimney? _____

4. A wooden plank measures 4m 58cm in length.
   What is the total length of 6 similar planks? _____

5. A piece of wire 9m 84cm long was cut into 4 equal pieces.
   What was the length of each piece? _____

6. A tree is 6·43m tall.
   Jim is 1m 48cm tall and Eric is 159cm tall.
   How much taller is the tree than the total height of the two boys? _____

7. A builder was building a wall 34m 63cm long.
   He built $9\frac{7}{10}$m one day and 13·85m the next day.
   What length of wall had he still to build? _____

8. Joe cycled 12km 565m one day and $9\frac{3}{4}$km the next day.
   How many km altogether did he cycle over the two days? _____

9. Jack set off on a 7·5km walk.
   When he had completed 5km 835m, how far had he still to go? _____

10. A racetrack is 3km 685m in length.
    Peter cycled around the racetrack 5 times.
    What distance did he cycle? _____

11. Paul walked 2km 345m.
    He travelled 4 times that distance on the bus.
    How far did he travel altogether? _____

12. The perimeter of a square is 9m 56cm.
    What is the length of each side? _____

22. Data

1.

 7   9   6   10

These are the number of football cards each child has.
If the cards were shared equally, each would have _____ cards.
The **average** number of cards is _____.

2. The ages of three children are 7 years, 8 years and 12 years.
What is their average age? _____

3. Joe had €12, Ann had €10 and Tom had €8 going shopping.
What was the average amount? _____

4. Paul spent 14 minutes, Pam spent 13 minutes and
Joan spent 9 minutes solving a puzzle.
What was the average time spent solving the puzzle? _____

5. Pat brought 12 bottles, Alan brought 17 bottles and Cora brought 10 bottles
to the bottle bank. What was the average number brought? _____

6. The average of 3 numbers is 12. Two of the numbers are 7 and 13.
What is the third number? _____

$12 \times 3 =$
$7 + 13 =$

7. This **bar chart** shows the ages of 5 children.

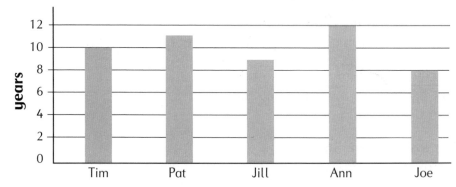

(a) What is the average age of the children? _____

(b) How many children are older than the average? _____

(c) How many children are younger than the average? _____

(d) Which child's age is the same as the average? _____

8. This table shows how 4 teams finished in a soccer league
(**win** = 3 points; **draw** = 1 point; **loss** = 0 points).

Team	P	W	D	L	F	A	Pts
Reds	12	8	1	3	25	8	25
Blues	12	7	2	3	22	10	23
Greens	12	6	2	4	18	11	20
Yellows	12	5	3	4	17	11	18

(a) Which team scored the most goals? _____

(b) Which team won the least number of matches? _____

(c) What was the goal difference (between **For** and **Against**) for each team?

    (i) Reds _____   **(ii)** Blues _____   **(iii)** Greens _____   **(iv)** Yellows _____

(d) How many more points did the Reds have than the Yellows? _____

(e) What was the average number of goals scored against the four teams? _____

(f) How many matches in total were won by the 4 teams? _____

(g) How many matches in total were lost by the 4 teams? _____

9. The boys and girls in Fifth Class were asked to select the **four sports** they like best from a list of **five**.

Here are the results.

sport	hurling	football	tennis	athletics	soccer
boys	12	14	9	8	13
girls	10	12	14	9	11

Show this information on a **multiple bar chart** (the first two are already done).

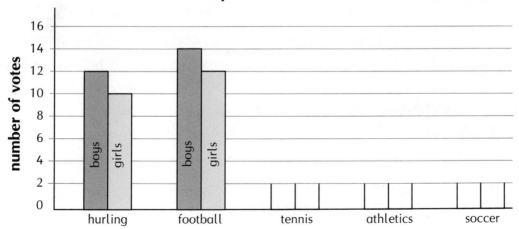

10. These questions are based on the **multiple bar chart** of children's best-liked sports in question 9.

(a) Which sport was most popular with (i) boys? _____ (ii) girls? _____

(b) Which sport was least popular with (i) boys? _____ (ii) girls? _____

(c) Which was the most popular sport overall? _____

(d) Which was the second most popular sport overall? _____

(e) How many votes in total were cast by the boys? _____

(f) How many votes in total were cast by the girls? _____

(g) Noting that each child had 4 votes,
how many children are there in the class? _____

11. This **pie chart** shows the favourite fruit of a group of **24 children**.

(a) How many children prefer the apple? _____

(b) How many children prefer the banana? _____

(c) How many children prefer the pear? _____

(d) What fraction of the children prefer the orange? _____

(e) What percentage of the children prefer the apple? _____

(f) What decimal fraction of the children prefer the banana? _____

12. This **pie chart** represents the hair colouring for a group of **36 children**.

(a) How many children have brown hair? _____

(b) How many children have red hair? _____

(c) What fraction of the children have fair hair? _____

(d) What percentage of the children have black hair? _____

(e) Twice as many children have _____ hair as have red hair.

13. A group of **16 children** was asked to name their favourite colour.
Here is how they voted: red **8**; green **4**; blue **2**; yellow **2**.

(a) Show this information on the pie chart.

(b) What fraction of the children prefer yellow? _____

(c) What percentage of the children prefer green? _____

23. Weight

Mental Computation

1. Write as **grammes**.
   (a) 1kg 300g   (b) 2kg 450g   (c) 2kg 185g   (d) 3kg 675g
   _____   _____   _____   _____

   (e) $2\frac{1}{2}$ kg   (f) $3\frac{1}{4}$ kg   (g) $4\frac{3}{4}$ kg   (h) $3\frac{7}{10}$ kg
   _____   _____   _____   _____

2. Write as **grammes**.
   (a) 2·48kg   (b) 3·76kg   (c) 4·9kg   (d) 2·08kg
   _____   _____   _____   _____

   (e) 1·375kg   (f) 4·59kg   (g) 6·7kg   (h) 5·065kg
   _____   _____   _____   _____

3. Write as **kilogrammes** using the **decimal point**.
   (a) 2700g   (b) 1980g   (c) 2095g   (d) 4006g
   _____   _____   _____   _____

   (e) 2kg 600g   (f) 3kg 670g   (g) 4kg 945g   (h) 1kg 85g
   _____   _____   _____   _____

4. How many **grammes** must be added to each of these to make **1kg**?
   (a) 460g   (b) 725g   (c) 645g   (d) 565g
   _____   _____   _____   _____

   (e) 0·75kg   (f) 0·885kg   (g) 0·065kg   (h) 0·64kg
   _____   _____   _____   _____

5. Write as **kilogrammes** and **grammes**.
   (a) 1785g   (b) 2384g   (c) 4078g   (d) 5009g
   _____   _____   _____   _____

   (e) $3\frac{1}{2}$ kg   (f) $2\frac{1}{4}$ kg   (g) $1\frac{3}{4}$ kg   (h) $2\frac{7}{10}$ kg
   _____   _____   _____   _____

6. Write as **kilogrammes** and **fractions** of a **kilogramme**.
   (a) 2300g   (b) 2030g   (c) 2003g   (d) 2250g
   _____   _____   _____   _____

   (e) 3600g   (f) 6750g   (g) 4090g   (h) 3007g
   _____   _____   _____   _____

Written Computation

1. 2·425kg
    3·685kg
    + 1·735kg
    _____

2. 3·685kg
    2·734kg
    + 1·586kg
    _____

3. 1·678kg
    2·739kg
    + 3·924kg
    _____

4. 4·367kg
    2·586kg
    + 1·392kg
    _____

5. 3·089kg
    2·768kg
    + 2·943kg
    _____

6. 8·927kg
    − 3·568kg
    _____

7. 9·243kg
    − 4·586kg
    _____

8. 6·425kg
    − 1·738kg
    _____

9. 7·034kg
    − 3·256kg
    _____

10. 9·005kg
    − 4·687kg
    _____

11. 1·735kg
    × 3
    _____

12. 1·497kg
    × 6
    _____

13. 2·438kg
    × 4
    _____

14. 1·036kg
    × 8
    _____

15. 1·209kg
    × 7
    _____

16. 5$\overline{)3\cdot975\text{kg}}$

17. 3$\overline{)7\cdot926\text{kg}}$

18. 4$\overline{)9\cdot372\text{kg}}$

19. 6$\overline{)8\cdot574\text{kg}}$

20. 7$\overline{)6\cdot797\text{kg}}$

Before doing these, write each in **decimal form**.

21. $2\text{kg } 380\text{g} + 1785\text{g} + 4\frac{1}{2}\text{kg} = $ _____

22. $2364\text{g} + 2\text{kg } 576\text{g} + 3\frac{1}{4}\text{kg} = $ _____

23. $1\frac{7}{10}\text{kg} + 2798\text{g} + 3\frac{1}{5}\text{kg} = $ _____

24. $2549\text{g} + 3\text{kg } 78\text{g} + 1\frac{3}{4}\text{kg} = $ _____

25. $(2\frac{9}{10}\text{kg} + 6243\text{g}) - 7\text{kg } 678\text{g} = $ _____

26. $(3\frac{3}{4}\text{kg} + 5076\text{g}) - 6\text{kg } 98\text{g} = $ _____

27. $(1\frac{1}{4}\text{kg} + 76\text{g}) \times 5 = $ _____

28. $(3\frac{7}{10}\text{kg} + 1\text{kg } 84\text{g}) \times 2 = $ _____

29. $(9\text{kg } 278\text{g} - 3\frac{3}{4}\text{kg}) \div 2 = $ _____

30. $(8\text{kg } 175\text{g} - 2\frac{9}{10}\text{kg}) \div 5 = $ _____

Mental Problems

1.  A parcel weighs $2\frac{1}{4}$ kg.
How many grammes does the parcel weigh? _____

2.  A box weighs 1·675kg.
How many grammes must be added so that it weighs 2kg? _____

3.  How many 125 gramme weights are needed
to balance a 1kg weight? _____

4.  How much would 1kg of grapes cost
if 250g cost €1·25? _____

5.  How much would 2kg of sugar cost
if 250g of sugar cost 50c? _____

6.  750 grammes of tomatoes cost €1·50.
How much should 1kg of tomatoes cost? _____

7.  How many bags of salt, each weighing 500g,
can be filled from a box that holds 3·5kg? _____

8.  Bananas cost €2·00 per kg.
How much should 600 grammes of bananas cost? _____

9.  How many bags of sweets, each weighing 300g,
can be filled from a box that holds 2·7kg? _____

10.  350 grammes of coffee cost €3·20.
How much should 1·4kg of coffee cost? _____

11. Tea costs €3·00 per 250g.
What change did I get from €20
when I bought $1\frac{1}{2}$kg of tea? _____

12. What change did I get from €5·00
when I bought 2·4kg of apples at €1·20 per 600g? _____

Written Problems

1. Jack weighs 43·76kg and Emma weighs $39\frac{3}{5}$ kg.
   What is the total weight of the two children? _____

2. One parcel weighs 8·36kg. Another parcel weighs $5\frac{3}{4}$ kg.
   What is the difference in weight between the two parcels? _____

3. A box of mushrooms weighs 1·365kg.
   What is the total weight of 7 boxes of mushrooms? _____

4. The total weight of the three boxes is 17·135kg.
   Two of the boxes weigh $7\frac{3}{10}$ kg and 6kg 378g.
   What is the weight of the third box? _____

5. The total weight of 3 hens is 5·775kg.
   What is the average weight of a hen? _____

6. A turkey weighs 9kg 685g.
   What is the total weight of 7 similar turkeys? _____

7. Salt costs 96c per 300g.
   How much should 2·4kg of salt cost? _____

8. A bag of sweets weighing 250g costs €1·28.
   How much should a box holding $1\frac{3}{4}$ kg of sweets cost? _____

9. Bananas cost €1·80 per kg.
   What change did I get from €10·00
   when I bought 3·5kg of bananas? _____

10. Meat costs €11·84 per kg.
    How much would $2\frac{1}{4}$ kg of meat cost? _____

11. Coffee costs €2·85 per 300g.
    What change did I get from €20·00
    when I bought 1·8kg of coffee? _____

12. Oranges cost €1·59 per 450 grammes.
    How much would 3·6kg of oranges cost? _____

24. Algebra

A. Directed Numbers

Numbers can be **positive** or **negative**.
Numbers **greater** than 0 are positive.
Numbers **less** than 0 are negative.
We write **positive 8** like this ⁺8 and **negative 8** like this ⁻8.

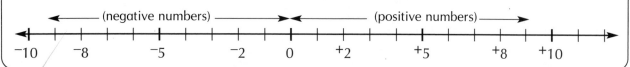

1. How many steps is it from ⁻5 to ⁺5? _____
2. How many steps is it from ⁺10 to ⁻2? _____
3. How many steps is it from ⁻7 to ⁺10? _____
4. How many steps is it from ⁺10 to ⁻10? _____
5. How many steps is it from ⁻8 to ⁻1? _____

A thermometer has **positive** and **negative** numbers.
At zero degrees (0°), water starts to freeze.
At 100° Celsius (100°C) water boils.

On a very cold night in Ireland, the temperature
could be as low as ⁻10°C, while on a hot summer's day,
the temperature in Ireland could be as high as ⁺30°.

6. How many degrees hotter is
   (a) ⁺30° than ⁺14°? _____   (b) ⁺23° than ⁺9°? _____
   (c) ⁺7° than ⁻2°? _____   (d) ⁺3° than ⁻9°? _____
   (e) ⁺18° than ⁻7°? _____   (f) ⁻2° than ⁻10°? _____
   (g) ⁻3° than ⁻8°? _____   (h) ⁺5° than ⁻7°? _____

7. What is the difference between
   (a) ⁺28 and ⁺13? _____   (b) ⁺13 and ⁻2? _____
   (c) ⁺9 and ⁻9? _____   (d) ⁻3 and ⁻12? _____
   (e) ⁺30 and ⁻10? _____   (f) ⁻8 and ⁻25? _____
   (g) ⁻7 and ⁺14? _____   (h) ⁻32 and ⁻20? _____

> **Video counters**, **calculator displays** and **lifts** in tall buildings can have **positive** and **negative** numbers.
>
> We regard our **money affairs** as being **positive** or **negative**, depending on whether we **have** money or **owe** money.

8. If a video counter is showing ⁻27 minutes, how many minutes to go before it shows ⁺12 minutes? _____

9. If a calculator displays ⁻35, how much must I add to have it display ⁺30? _____

10. A lift in a tall building goes from the 26th floor (⁺26) to the 5th floor (⁻5) below ground level. What distance in floors does it travel? _____

11. Avril has €19. Andrew owes €35 to the bank. How many Euro better off is Avril than Andrew? _____

B. Rules and Properties

Work out the pattern and write the next **three** numbers in each of these.

1. 8, 16, 24, 32, ____, ____, ____
2. 55, 50, 45, 40, ____, ____, ____
3. 4, 10, 16, 22, ____, ____, ____
4. 84, 77, 70, 63, ____, ____, ____
5. 1, 4, 9, 16, ____, ____, ____
6. 2, 4, 8, 16, ____, ____, ____
7. 1·5, 3, 4·5, 6, ____, ____, ____
8. 1, 3, 6, 10, ____, ____, ____
9. 1, 4, 10, 19, ____, ____, ____
10. 1, 3, 7, 13, ____, ____, ____

Write the answers to each of these.

11. $16 - 7 + 8 =$ _____
12. $16 - (7 + 8) =$ _____
13. $20 - 9 + 5 =$ _____
14. $20 - (9 + 5) =$ _____
15. $25 - 8 + 4 =$ _____
16. $25 - (8 + 4) =$ _____
17. $(3 \times 4) + 6 =$ _____
18. $3 \times (4 + 6) =$ _____
19. $(2 \times 8) - 5 =$ _____
20. $2 \times (8 - 5) =$ _____
21. $(7 \times 6) - 4 =$ _____
22. $7 \times (6 - 4) =$ _____
23. $(9 \times 2) + 6 =$ _____
24. $9 \times (2 + 6) =$ _____
25. $(6 \times 5) + 4 =$ _____
26. $6 \times (5 + 4) =$ _____
27. $(8 \times 7) - 2 =$ _____
28. $8 \times (7 - 2) =$ _____

29. **True** or **False**?
Where there are brackets, always do the part inside the brackets first. _____

30. **True** or **False**?
When there are no brackets, always do **multiplication** and **division** before **addition** and **subtraction**. _____

* When doing these, be careful to do the operations in the right order.

31. (a) $8 \times 7 + 6 =$ _____   (b) $7 + 9 \times 6 =$ _____   (c) $45 - 6 \times 7 =$ _____

32. (a) $54 \div 9 + 7 =$ _____   (b) $8 + 35 \div 5 =$ _____   (c) $9 \times 8 - 7 =$ _____

33. (a) $63 \div 7 - 4 =$ _____   (b) $75 - 8 \times 8 =$ _____   (c) $14 + 9 \times 5 =$ _____

34. (a) $8 \times 7 - 5 =$ _____   (b) $86 - 9 \times 9 =$ _____   (c) $56 \div 7 - 3 =$ _____

35. (a) $9 \times 10 + 7 =$ _____   (b) $78 - 72 \div 9 =$ _____   (c) $24 + 45 \div 5 =$ _____

* Use your **calculator** to help you to find the answers to these.

	(a)	(b)	(c)
36.	$28 + 54 \times 19 =$ _____	$63 \times 27 + 39 =$ _____	$45 \times 36 - 842 =$ _____
37.	$57 + 266 \div 7 =$ _____	$368 \div 8 + 96 =$ _____	$467 - 895 \div 5 =$ _____
38.	$364 \div 13 + 38 =$ _____	$712 - 78 \times 7 =$ _____	$36 \times 29 - 756 =$ _____
39.	$26 \cdot 7 \times 9 - 73 \cdot 6 =$ _____	$5 \cdot 79 + 8 \cdot 04 \div 6 =$ _____	$6 \cdot 24 - 9 \cdot 59 \div 7 =$ _____
40.	$928 \div 16 - 37 =$ _____	$821 - 19 \times 28 =$ _____	$35 \times 23 - 627 =$ _____

C. Equations

* Put the correct numbers in the frames to make each of these **mathematical sentences** true.

1. (a) $9 + \boxed{} = 16$ (b) $6 \times 8 = \boxed{}$ (c) $7 \times \boxed{} = 56$

2. (a) $54 \div 6 = \boxed{}$ (b) $40 \div \boxed{} = 8$ (c) $36 - \boxed{} = 29$

3. (a) $72 \div \boxed{} = 8$ (b) $63 \div 9 = \boxed{}$ (c) $53 + \boxed{} = 61$

4. (a) $76 - 34 = \boxed{}$ (b) $42 \div \boxed{} = 7$ (c) $\boxed{} \div 6 = 4$

5. (a) $\boxed{} \times 6 = 60$ (b) $\boxed{} - 36 = 9$ (c) $\boxed{} + 28 = 48$

* Put the correct **operation sign** (+, −, × or ÷) in the frames to make the following **mathematical sentences** true.

6. (a) $24 \boxed{} 7 = 31$ (b) $6 \boxed{} 5 = 30$ (c) $35 \boxed{} 8 = 27$

7. (a) $54 \boxed{} 6 = 9$ (b) $7 \boxed{} 8 = 56$ (c) $54 \boxed{} 19 = 35$

8. (a) $96 \boxed{} 8 = 12$ (b) $67 \boxed{} 12 = 79$ (c) $90 \boxed{} 10 = 9$

* Write each of the following as **equations**.

9. Thirty-five plus twenty-five equals sixty. _____

10. Sixty-eight plus four equals nine times eight. _____

11. Seven times five equals thirty plus five. _____

12. Sixty minus four equals eight times seven. _____

* Write each of the following in **equation form** using a frame.
  Calculate the number that goes in each frame.

13. Joe had twenty-five football cards.
His uncle gave him twelve. How many cards had he then? _____

14. Pat had forty-two nuts. He gave eight of them to Bill.
How many nuts had he left? _____

15. There are twelve apples in a bag. Ann sold five bags.
How many apples did she sell? _____

16. A teacher made teams of seven from a group of fifty-six children.
How many teams did she make? _____

* Solve the following equations.

17. (a) $\frac{1}{4}$ of 32 = _____   (b) $\frac{3}{4}$ of 24 = _____   (c) $\frac{2}{3}$ of 18 = _____

18. (a) $\frac{2}{5}$ of 35 = _____   (b) $\frac{4}{5}$ of 45 = _____   (c) $\frac{3}{5}$ of 40 = _____

19. (a) $\frac{5}{8}$ of 56 = _____   (b) $\frac{7}{8}$ of 48 = _____   (c) $\frac{3}{8}$ of 72 = _____

20. (a) $\frac{5}{6}$ of 36 = _____   (b) $\frac{4}{9}$ of 63 = _____   (c) $\frac{8}{9}$ of 54 = _____

21. (a) 0·3 of 60 = _____   (b) 0·7 of 50 = _____   (c) 0·9 of 90 = _____

22. (a) 0·5 of 18 = _____   (b) 0·25 of 28 = _____   (c) 0·75 of 36 = _____

23. (a) 10% of 80 = _____   (b) 40% of 50 = _____   (c) 25% of 28 = _____

24. (a) 50% of 36 = _____   (b) 75% of 32 = _____   (c) 60% of 25 = _____

* Write the correct operation sign (+, –, × **or** ÷) in the frames to make these sentences true.

25. (a) 6 ☐ (8 ☐ 2) = 36   (b) (7 ☐ 6) ☐ 5 = 47

26. (a) (13 ☐ 6) ☐ 5 = 35   (b) 9 ☐ (7 ☐ 3) = 30

27. (a) 4 ☐ (9 ☐ 6) = 7   (b) 50 ☐ (9 ☐ 4) = 14

28. (a) (70 ☐ 7) ☐ 5 = 50   (b) (21 ☐ 14) ☐ 6 = 42

25. Capacity

Eibhlis

Mental Computation

Write as **millilitres (ml)**.

1. 1l 275ml _____

2. 2l 65ml _____

3. $2\frac{1}{4}$ l _____

4. 2l 9ml _____

5. 3·57l _____

6. $3\frac{3}{4}$ l _____

7. 4·2l _____

8. 5·085l _____

Write as **litres** using the **decimal point**.

9. 1730ml _____

10. 2075ml _____

11. 2l 96ml _____

12. 3l 8ml _____

13. $2\frac{3}{10}$ l _____

14. $3\frac{7}{100}$ l _____

15. $1\frac{9}{1000}$ l _____

16. $2\frac{183}{1000}$ l _____

What must be **added** to each of these to make **1 litre**?

17. 670ml _____

18. 585ml _____

19. 0·85l _____

20. 0·075l _____

Written Computation

1.
$$3\cdot796l \\ + 5\cdot478l$$

2.
$$4\cdot687l \\ + 2\cdot925l$$

3.
$$9\cdot364l \\ - 6\cdot238l$$

4.
$$8\cdot605l \\ - 3\cdot728l$$

5.
$$9\cdot003l \\ - 6\cdot387l$$

6.
$$1\cdot675l \\ \times 3$$

7.
$$1\cdot438l \\ \times 6$$

8.
$$2\cdot347l \\ \times 4$$

9.
$$1\cdot075l \\ \times 8$$

10.
$$1\cdot308l \\ \times 7$$

11. $5\overline{)4\cdot865l}$

12. $4\overline{)6\cdot396l}$

13. $3\overline{)7\cdot284l}$

14. $6\overline{)7\cdot458l}$

15. $7\overline{)7\cdot693l}$

83

Before doing these write each in decimal form.

16. $2l\ 375ml + 2067ml + 3\frac{1}{2}l = $ _____

17. $2\frac{7}{10} + 2805ml + 1\frac{3}{4}l = $ _____

18. $(6387ml + 2\frac{1}{4}l) - 7l\ 896ml = $ _____

19. $(2\frac{3}{4}l + 98ml) \times 3 = $ _____

20. $(9l\ 635ml - 3\frac{9}{10}l) \div 5 = $ _____

Mental Problems

1.  A container holds $3\frac{1}{4}$ litres.
How many millilitres does the container hold? _____

2. A kettle holds 1·765l.
How many ml must be added to the kettle to make 2 litres? _____

3. How many 250ml bottles can be filled from a container
that holds 2 litres? _____

4. How much should 2 litres of orange cost
if 500ml of orange cost 60c? _____

5. 750ml of lemon cost €1·50.
How much should half a litre of lemon cost? _____

6. How many 500ml bottles can be filled from a container
that holds 4·5 litres? _____

7. What should be the cost of a litre of cream
if 250ml of cream cost €1·20? _____

8. Petrol costs 95c per litre.
How much should 20 litres of petrol cost? _____

9. 300ml of paint thinner cost €1·50.
How much should 1·8 litres of paint thinner cost? _____

10.  An oil tank was filled with 900 litres of oil.
What was the cost of the oil at 50c per litre? _____

11.  How much cheaper is a 2-litre bottle of cola costing €2
than four 500ml bottles costing 70c each? _____

12.  Orange juice costs €1·50 per 600ml. What change did I get from €8
when I bought 3 litres of orange juice? _____

Written Problems

1. A container holds 6·85 litres of water.
Another container holds $5\frac{2}{5}$ litres.
What is the total capacity of the two containers? _____

2. When 2l 375ml was poured from a jar that held 5·8 litres,
how much remained in the jar? _____

3. A basin holds 1·485 litres.
What is the total capacity of 5 similar basins? _____

4. The total capacity of three containers is 16·145l.
Two of the containers hold $5\frac{7}{10}$l and 6l 325ml.
What is the capacity of the third container? _____

5. The total capacity of four kettles is 9·376l.
What is the average capacity of a kettle? _____

6. Apple juice costs 89c per 400ml.
How much should 2·4 litres of apple juice cost? _____

7. 250ml of grapefruit juice costs €0·78.
How much should $1\frac{3}{4}$ litres of the juice cost? _____

8. Cooking oil costs €2·74 per litre.
How much should $3\frac{1}{2}$ litres cost? _____

9. Lemonade costs 67c per 300ml.
What change did I get from €5
when I bought 1·5 litres of lemonade? _____

10. 500ml of paint costs €2·65.
How much had I left from €20 when I bought 3·5 litres of paint? _____

11. How much cheaper is a $2\frac{1}{2}$ litre container of orange juice
costing €7·49 than five 500ml containers costing €1·85 each? _____

12. Shampoo costs €2·89 per 600ml.
What change did a hairstylist get from €20·00
when he bought 3·6 litres of shampoo? _____

26. Chance

Tossing Coins

1. If I toss a coin, the outcome must be either **heads** or **tails**. If I get **heads** the first time, there is no guarantee that I will get **tails** the next time. Each toss is completely independent of the previous ones. It is complete chance.

(a) If you toss a coin **100 times**, how many **heads** and how many **tails** would you expect to get?   heads _____ tails _____

(b) Do you think it will always work out like this? _____

(c) **True** or **False**? Each time I toss, I have a 50% chance of getting **heads**. _____

(d) 50% chance means **one** chance in _____ or fifty / fifty **or** an even chance.

2. If I toss **two coins**, I have **three** possible outcomes (**2** heads, **2** tails, head and tail).

(a) Toss two coins **40 times** and record the results on a frequency table.

frequency table		
outcome	tally	total
2 heads		
2 tails		
head and tail		

(b) Do you think each pupil got the same result? _____

(c) Do you think you would get the same result if you repeated your experiment? _____

(d) Each time you toss, do you think you have an **even chance**, a **1 chance in 3** or a **1 chance in 4** of getting

(i) 2 heads?   **(ii)** 2 tails?   **(iii)** head and tail?

_____   _____   _____

(e) Why do you think you have a greater chance of getting a head and tail?

_____

3. Rolling a Dice

(a) Each time I roll a dice there are _____ possible outcomes.

(b) How often would you expect to get a four? _____ chance in 6.

(c) **True** or **False**? Every time I roll the dice, each of the six numbers has an equal chance of winning. _____

(d) The chances of rolling an even number are _____ in two.

(e) **True** or **False**? Each time I roll the dice, I have a fifty-fifty chance of getting an odd number. _____

4. Coloured Cubes

In a bag, place **5** red cubes, **3** yellow cubes and **2** blue cubes. Draw a cube from the bag and record the outcome on a frequency table for a total of 30 draws.

frequency table		
colour	tally	total
red		
yellow		
blue		

(a) Which colour came out most often? _____

(b) How many times did you draw yellow? _____

(c) How many times did you draw blue? _____

(d) If you repeat the experiment, will you get the same result? _____

(e) What are the chances of drawing a red cube? _____

(f) What are the chances of drawing a yellow cube? _____

(g) What are the chances of drawing a blue cube? _____

5.

In a bag, there are **4** green marbles, **3** blue marbles, **2** red marbles and **1** yellow marble.

(i) If I draw a marble from the bag, what are the chances of it being

(a) a green marble? _____   (b) a blue marble? _____

(c) a red marble? _____   (d) a yellow marble? _____

(ii) If I make a total of **50 draws**, how many times would I expect to draw

(a) a green marble? _____   (b) a blue marble? _____

(c) a red marble? _____   (d) a yellow marble? _____

6. Spinners

> This spinner has **8 segments**.
> Each segment has the name of a county written on it.
> Some counties are included more than once. →

When I spin the spinner, what are the chances of it landing on

(a) Clare?   **(b)** Cork?   **(c)** Galway?   **(d)** Dublin?

_____   _____   _____   _____

(e) Which county is **3 times** as likely to win as Galway? _____

(f) Which county has an **equal chance** of winning as Dublin? _____

(g) If I spin the spinner thirty times, is it certain that Cork will be the winner overall? _____

7. A survey of the **favourite fruit** of a group of children produced the following table.

fruit	no. of children who preferred it
apple	40
orange	25
pear	20
banana	15

(a) How many children were included in the survey? _____

(b) Which fruit was the most popular? _____

(c) Which fruit was the favourite of 20 of the children? _____

If I ask a child from the group to name his / her favourite fruit

(d) what are the chances of it being apple? _____

(e) what are the chances of it being orange? _____

(f) what are the chances of it being pear? _____

(g) what are the chances of it being banana? _____

8. Here is the result of a survey of the favourite sport of a group of children.
Gaelic Football **8**, Soccer **5**, Hurling **4**, Tennis **3**.

If I ask a child from the group to name his / her favourite sport

(a) there is a _____ in _____ chance it will be Gaelic Football.

(b) there is a _____ in _____ chance it will be Soccer.

(c) there is a _____ in _____ chance it will be Hurling.

(d) there is a _____ in _____ chance it will be Tennis.

27. Test Yourself 2

Mental Computation

1. $(9 \times 7) + 8 =$ _____
2. $(12 \times 8) + 6 =$ _____
3. $(10 \times 11) + 9 =$ _____
4. $58 \div 9 =$ ___R___
5. $79 \div 8 =$ ___R___
6. $53 \div 6 =$ ___R___
7. $\frac{3}{4} = \frac{}{12}$
8. $\frac{2}{3} = \frac{}{12}$
9. $\frac{5}{6} = \frac{}{12}$
10. $\frac{4}{5} = \frac{}{10}$

Write as **mixed numbers**.

11. $\frac{14}{3} =$ _____
12. $\frac{29}{6} =$ _____
13. $\frac{31}{8} =$ _____
14. $\frac{53}{9} =$ _____

Write as **decimal fractions**.

15. $\frac{7}{10} =$ _____
16. $\frac{9}{100} =$ _____
17. $\frac{3}{1000} =$ _____
18. $\frac{17}{1000} =$ _____
19. $\frac{1}{2} =$ _____
20. $\frac{1}{4} =$ _____
21. $\frac{3}{4} =$ _____
22. $\frac{3}{5} =$ _____

Write these percentages as **fractions** in their **lowest terms**.

23. $50\% =$ _____
24. $75\% =$ _____
25. $40\% =$ _____
26. $5\% =$ _____
27. 25% of $36 =$ _____
28. 20% of $30 =$ _____
29. 60% of $35 =$ _____
30. 15% of $80 =$ _____

Score [ ] /30

Written Computation

1. $1\frac{5}{6} + 2\frac{7}{12} =$ _____
2. $1\frac{5}{12} + 3\frac{3}{4} =$ _____
3. $3\frac{2}{3} + \frac{8}{9} =$ _____
4. $4\frac{3}{5} + 1\frac{9}{10} =$ _____
5. $5\frac{1}{2} - 2\frac{5}{6} =$ _____
6. $6\frac{1}{4} - 4\frac{5}{8} =$ _____
7. $\frac{3}{5} \times 7 =$ _____
8. $5 \times \frac{7}{9} =$ _____

9.
$$\begin{array}{r} 3\cdot287 \\ \times\ 6 \\ \hline \end{array}$$

10.
$$\begin{array}{r} 5\cdot497 \\ \times\ 8 \\ \hline \end{array}$$

11.
$$\begin{array}{r} 7\cdot689 \\ \times\ 9 \\ \hline \end{array}$$

12.
$$\begin{array}{r} 8\cdot476 \\ \times\ 7 \\ \hline \end{array}$$

13. $27\overline{)693}$
14. $43\overline{)984}$
15. $39\overline{)896}$
16. $38\overline{)904}$

Increase.

17. 384 by 25%
18. 495 by 20%
19. 570 by 30%
20. 278 by 50%

Score [ ] /20

89

Mental Problems

1. Joan has 72 stamps. Jack has $\frac{7}{8}$ of that number. How many stamps has Jack? _____

2. What change had Avril from €10·00 when she bought this football? _____

3. $\frac{3}{8}$ of the apples in a box were red. If there were 30 red apples, how many apples were there in the box altogether? _____

4. 8 bars cost €3·20. How much should 24 bars cost? _____

5. 0·7 of the people at a match were children. If 56 children attended, how many people altogether were at the match? _____

6. A farmer had 80 animals. 30% of these were cows. How many cows had she? _____

7. What number is 4020 greater than 53 960? _____

8. Mark has 7 marbles and Mandy has 28 marbles. Express Mark's number as a percentage of Mandy's number. _____

9. I spent $\frac{3}{5}$ of my money in one shop and 0·15 of it in another. What percentage of my money had I left? _____

10. There were 80 oranges in a box. 5% of these were bad. How many bad oranges were there? _____

11. Last year a jersey cost €55. It is 20% more expensive this year. How much does it cost this year? _____

12. During a sale, a pair of football boots, normally costing €84 were reduced in price by 25%. What was the sale price? _____

Score [/12]

90

Written Problems

1. A cinema ticket costs €8·65.
   What is the total cost of 9 cinema tickets? _____

2. A bicycle costs €94·35. Jill had €38·67.
   Her Mam gave her €43·12.
   How much more does she need to buy the bicycle? _____

3. Five packets of sweets cost €9·65.
   How much should three packets of sweets cost? _____

4. Jim spent $\frac{3}{8}$ of his money buying a helmet.
   If he had €19·45 left, how much had he at first? _____

5. An aeroplane can carry 379 passengers.
   How many passengers can 28 aeroplanes carry? _____

6. A bus can carry 47 passengers.
   How many buses are needed to carry 893 passengers? _____

7. There were 626 oranges in a box.
   14 of these were bad.
   The remainder were packed into bags of 18.
   How many bags were filled? _____

8. A tradesman had $7\frac{5}{12}$ rolls of wallpaper. He used $2\frac{3}{4}$ rolls.
   How many rolls of wallpaper had he left? _____

9. 3 children each ate $\frac{7}{8}$ of a bar of chocolate.
   How many bars of chocolate did they eat altogether? _____

10. A farmer sold 0·7 of her animals and had 87 animals left.
    How many animals had she at first? _____

11. 985 people attended a concert last year.
    20% more people attended this year.
    How many attended this year? _____

12. Last year a TV set cost €576.
    It costs 25% less this year.
    How much does it cost this year? _____

Score [/12]

91

28. Test Yourself 3

Mental Computation

Write as **hours** and **minutes**.

1. 78 mins _____

2. 111 mins _____

3. 147 mins _____

4. 169 mins _____

Write these times using the **24-hour** system (**4 digits**).

5. 4.25 am _____

6. 1.45 pm _____

7. 7.38 pm _____

8. 9.54 pm _____

Write as **km** in **decimal form**.

9. 2km 75m _____

10. 3km 8m _____

11. 5760m _____

12. $4\frac{19}{1000}$km _____

13. 0·3 of 70 = _____

14. 0·7 of 80 = _____

15. 0·4 of 35 = _____

16. 0·25 of 24 = _____

17. 50% of 46 = _____

18. 75% of 28 = _____

19. 20% of 45 = _____

20. 60% of 35 = _____

21. 5% of 60 = _____

22. 15% of 80 = _____

23. 7% of 200 = _____

24. 4% of 300 = _____

25. 625g + _____g = 1kg

26. 2·06kg = _____g

27. $1\frac{3}{4}$kg = _____g

28. 485ml + _____ml = 1l

29. 1·7l = _____ml

30. $1\frac{3}{5}$l = _____ml

Score [____ /30]

Written Computation

1. €19·76 × 3

2. €17·98 × 4

3. €18·67 × 5

4. €13·58 × 7

5. €15·89 × 6

6. 3)€19·74

7. 5)€28·65

8. 4)€35·72

9. 6)€46·38

10. 8)€59·36

11. 28)735

12. 34)926

13. 46)978

14. 37)806

15. 19)769

16. Find the average of 23, 19, 27 and 15. _____

17. Increase 436 by 25% _____   **18.** Increase 290 by 30% _____

19. Decrease 645 by 20% _____   **20.** Decrease 852 by 25% _____

Score [/20]

Mental Problems

1. What change had Alex from €20
when he bought the hurley? _____

€16·65

2. 0·3 of the people at a film were adults.
If 36 adults attended,
how many people altogether were at the film? _____

CINEMA

3. I spent $\frac{2}{5}$ of my money in one shop and 0·25 of it in another.
What percentage of my money had I left? _____

Newsagent

4. A train left the station at 14:35.
If the journey lasted $2\frac{1}{2}$ hours, at what time did it end? _____

5. A garden shed is 5m long and 3m wide.
What is the area of the shed floor? _____

6. The perimeter of a rectangle is 40cm.
If its length is 12cm, what is its area? _____

12cm

7. Having spent 0·25 of his money, Pat had €24 left.
How much had he at first? _____

SHOP

8. How many 500ml bottles of water can be filled from a container
that holds 6·5 litres? _____

water 500ml   water 500ml

9. Tea costs €2·50 per 250g.
What change had I from €20·00
when I bought 1·75kg of tea? _____

TEA

10. Liz spent 75% of her money on a bicycle and had €40 left.
What was the cost of the bicycle? _____

11. What change had I from €5·00
when I bought 1·6kg of apples at €1·15 per 400g? _____

12. How much will I save by buying
a 2 litre bottle of orange costing €2
instead of four 500ml bottles costing 60c each? _____

€2

ORANGE
2l

Score [/12]

93

Written Problems

1. CINEMA
   A film started at 14:53.
   If the film lasted 2 hrs 19 mins, at what time did it end? _____

2. 27m
   The perimeter of a rectangular lawn is 90m.
   If its length is 27m, what is its area? _____

3. What will it cost to fence in a garden 19m long and 12m wide
   if fencing costs €15 per metre? _____

4. David cycled 9km 485m one day and $8\frac{3}{4}$km the next day.
   How many km altogether did he cycle over the two days? _____

5. Bananas cost €1·60 per kg.
   What change had I from €10
   when I bought 4·5kg of bananas? _____

6. Coffee costs €2·75 per 300g.
   What change had I from €20
   when I bought 1·5kg of coffee? _____

7. The total capacity of four kettles is 9·736l.
   What is the average capacity of a kettle? _____

8. How much will I save by buying a $2\frac{1}{2}$ litre container of orange
   for €6·85 instead of five 500ml bottles costing €1·65 each? _____

9. A football manager had €126 change from €1000 when he bought
   19 football jerseys. How much did each jersey cost? _____

10. Andrew spent 0·6 of his money buying clothes.
    If he had €72 left, how much did he spend on clothes? _____

11. During a sale, a digital camera was reduced in price by 20%.
    If the normal price was €285, what was the sale price? _____

12. A car travels 15km on 1 litre of petrol.
    What is the cost of the petrol for a journey of
    120km at €0·97 per litre? _____

Score [/12]

94